Houghton Mifflin

California Math

Homework and Problem Solving

Student Book

- **Homework**
- **Leveled Problem Solving**

GRADE

5

 HOUGHTON MIFFLIN   BOSTON

Printed in the U.S.A.

ISBN 10: 0-618-96132-1
ISBN 13: 978-0-618-96132-0

   16 17 18 0982 16 15 14 13
4500418268

Hands On: Find Prime Numbers

CA Standard
KEY NS 1.4

Can Jules arrange 8 blocks in one or more rows with an equal number of blocks in each row? To find out, decide whether 8 is prime or not prime.

Prime numbers have exactly two different factors: 1 and itself.	
Is 8 a prime number?	8 has more than two factors (1 and itself), so it is **not** a prime number.
Ask yourself: How many ways could I arrange 8 tiles?	■■■■■■■■ ■■■■ ■■■■ (array of 8)
Jules can arrange the 8 blocks in more than one way, so 8 is not a prime number.	

Decide if the number is prime or not prime. You can draw arrays or use your completed table.

1. 6

_____

2. 11

_____

3. 27

_____

4. 42

_____

5. 19

_____

6. 31

_____

7. 24

_____

8. 37

_____

9. 13

_____

Spiral Review   (Grade 4, Chapter 7, Lesson 2) **KEY** 4 AF 1.2, 4 AF 1.3

Simplify.

10. $4 + (5 - 2)$
_____

11. $(42 - 27) \times 2$
_____

12. Forty-five students were on a bus on the way home from school. Twelve students got off the bus at the first stop, how many people are now on the bus including the bus driver?

_____

Hands On: Find Prime Numbers

CA Standard
KEY NS 1.4

Decide if the number is *prime* or *not prime*. You can draw arrays or use your completed table.

1. Look at the array for the number 5. Is 5 prime or not prime?

   _____

2. Look at the arrays for the number 14. Is 14 prime or not prime?

3. Mr. Kelvin wants to arrange 17 tiles into equal rows and columns, but he continues to have an extra tile no matter how he arranges them. Why is Mr. Kelvin having this problem?

   _____

   _____

   _____

4. Jason is arranging his 18 baseball cards into equal rows and columns. Draw arrays to show Jason all the possible ways he could arrange his baseball cards. Is 18 prime or not prime? Explain.

   _____

   _____

   _____

5. In Mrs. Kendall's class the desks are arranged in 6 rows of 6 desks. How many desks are in Mrs. Kendall's class, and is the number prime or not prime? Explain.

   _____

   _____

   _____

   _____

6. A rug is covered with 12" × 12" squares as seen below. What is the area of the rug in square feet? Is the area prime?

   _____

   _____

Find Factors of a Number

Can Jules arrange 9 blocks in one or more rows with an equal number of blocks in each row? To find out, decide whether 9 is prime or not prime.

Different Ways to Find Factors of 9	
Way 1 Draw all the ways you can arrange 9 squares in an array.	**Way 2** Use division Divide by 1. $9 \div 1 = 9$ 1 and 9 are factors of 9. Divide by 3 $9 \div 3 = 3$ 3 is a factor of 9.

Solution: The factors of 9 are 1, 3 and 9. So, 9 is a composite number.

Draw arrays to find the factors of each number. Write if the number is *prime* or *composite*.

1. 9

2. 16

3. 20

Use division to find the factors of each number. Then write if the number is *prime* or *composite*.

4. 42

5. 45

6. 49

Spiral Review (Grade 4, Chapter 7, Lesson 2) **KEY 4 AF 1.2, 4 AF 1.3**

Simplify.

7. $8 + (4 \times 2)$ _____

8. $25 - (5 + 2)$ _____

9. Calvin buys 7 baseball cards at the Cards Galore store and then gives 1 to his brother. If Calvin already owned 16 baseball cards, how many cards does Calvin now have?

Find Factors of a Number

CA Standards
KEY NS 1.4, MR 2.4

Solve problems 1–6.

1. I am a counting number that has more than two different types of factors. Am I a prime number or composite number?

_____

2. Jimmy arranged 9 tiles into three different arrays. What are the factors of the number 9?

_____

3. The sum of my ones and tens digit is 10. My tens digit is greater than my ones digit. I am a prime number. What number am I?

_____

4. Husam has 30 stamps. He wants to arrange them in equal rows. In how many ways can he arrange them?

_____

5. Mr. Jenkin's age is a composite number. The number in the ones place is the product of 2 × 4. The number in the tens place is the difference of half a dozen from one dozen. How old is Mr. Jenkins?

_____

6. The area of a rectangular hallway is 120 square feet. If the length and the width are both composite numbers, what are the possible dimensions of the hallway?

_____

Prime Factorization

CA Standards
KEY NS 1.4, MR 2.3

Write the prime factorization of 24.

Step ① Write 24 as the product of 2 factors.

24
4 × 6

Step ② Write the factors of each composite factor.

24
4 × 6

=

24
4 × 6
2×2 × 2×3

Step ③ Write the prime factors.

$24 = 2 \times 2 \times 2 \times 3$

Solution: The prime factorization of 24 is $2 \times 2 \times 2 \times 3$

Complete the factor tree. Then write the prime factorization.

1. 20
$2 \times \square$
$2 \times 2 \times \square$
$2 \times \square \times \square$

2. 20
$4 \times \square$
$\square \times 2 \times \square$
$\square \times \square \times \square$

Write the prime factorization of each number. If the number is prime, write _prime_.

3. 28

_____

4. 23

_____

5. 30

_____

6. 42

_____

7. 65

_____

8. 56

_____

Spiral Review   (Grade 4, Chapter 11, Lesson 4) **4 NS 3.3**

Simplify.

13. 185×32

_____

14. 340×28

_____

15. In the school library, there were 33 science books on each of the 17 shelves located in the science section. How many science books does the library own?

_____

Prime Factorization

CA Standards
KEY NS 1.4, MR 2.3

Use prime factorization to solve problems 1–6.

1. Complete the factor tree for the number 8.

_____

2. Rita's age is a prime number between 5 and 10. How old is Rita?

_____

3. Which number between 20 and 29 has 2 and 3 in its prime factorization?

_____

4. Which number between 29 and 39 has three different prime factors? What is the prime factorization of this number?

_____

5. Nathan bought a sandwich for $5.25, a soda for $1.50, and a bag of popcorn for $2.25. What is the prime factorization of the total amount he spent for his lunch?

_____

6. The basketball team scored points by making 8 free throws, worth one point each. The team also made 14 baskets, worth 2 points each. How many total points did the team score and what is the prime factorization of the score?

_____

Exponents and Prime Factorization

Use exponents to write the prime factorization of 32.

Step ① Write 32 as the product of 2 factors.

Step ② Write the factors of each composite factor.

Step ③ Identify the base or repeated factor. Count how many times the base is repeated to identify the exponent.

base: **2**; repeated 5 times

$2 \times 2 \times 2 \times 2 \times 2 = 32$

Solution: $2^5 = 32$

Write the prime factorization of each number. Use exponents if possible. If the number is prime, write *prime*.

1. 28

_____

2. 23

_____

3. 64

_____

4. 30

_____

5. 50

_____

6. 56

_____

Write each expression using exponents.

7. $2 \times 2 \times 2$

_____

8. $6 \times 6 \times 6 \times 6$

_____

9. $4 \times 4 \times 4$

_____

Spiral Review (Grade 4, Chapter 11, Lessons 3–4) **NS 3.2**

Add.

10. $\frac{1}{5} + \frac{2}{5} =$ _____

11. $\frac{2}{4} + \frac{2}{4} =$ _____

12. For breakfast, Madison ate $\frac{1}{3}$ of the granola bar in the cabinet. After school, Madison ate another $\frac{1}{3}$ of the bar. How many granola bars did Madison eat?

_____

Exponents and Prime Factorization

Use exponents and prime factorization to solve problems 1–6.

1. Maria bought 4 boxes of muffins with 16 muffins in each box. Write an expression using exponents to find how many muffins she bought.

_____

2. Use different factors to write the prime factorization for 24.

```
      24
     /  \
    3    8
        /  \
       2    4
           /  \
          2    2
```

_____

3. Which numbers between 40 and 49 have 2 and 3 in their prime factorization? Use exponents to write the prime factorization of each number.

_____

_____

4. Tony said the prime factorization of 72 is $2^3 \times 3^3$. Explain what Tony's mistake was. Then find the correct answer.

_____

_____

_____

_____

5. Four students bought school supplies. Each student filled their pencil boxes with 5 pencils, 2 erasers, 2 highlighters, and 1 glue stick. Write an expression to find how many supplies were purchased by all four students. Then, use exponents to write the prime factorization of this number.

_____

_____

_____

_____

6. The Davis' backyard measures 40 ft × 90 ft. Find the area of their backyard and show how the area could be written using exponents.

_____

_____

Name _____ Date _____

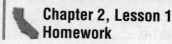
Hands On: Represent Fractions

CA Standards
KEY NS 1.5, MR 2.3

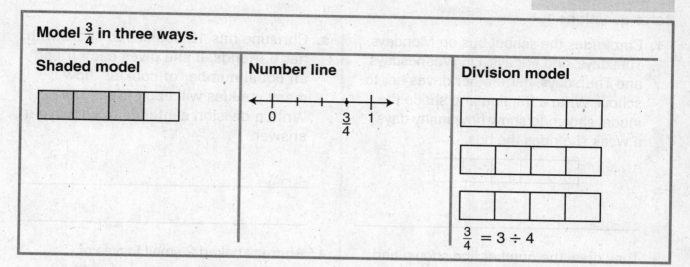

Draw a shaded model for each fraction.

1. $\frac{2}{3}$

2. $\frac{5}{7}$

3. $\frac{3}{10}$

Draw a number line and show the position of each fraction.

4. $\frac{2}{5}$

5. $\frac{7}{5}$

6. $\frac{11}{5}$

Draw a model to show each fraction as a division expression. Write the division expression.

7. $\frac{6}{2}$

8. $\frac{5}{3}$

Spiral Review (Chapter 1, Lesson 4) NS 1.3, **KEY** NS 1.4

Find the prime factorization for each number. Use exponents.

9. 24 _____

10. 56 _____

11. 48 _____

12. A teacher wants to write 15 problems on the board. How can he write the problems in equal rows?

_____

Hands On: Represent Fractions

CA Standards
KEY NS 1.5, MR 2.3

Solve questions 1–6.

1. Carol rides the school bus on Mondays, Tuesdays, and Fridays. On Wednesdays and Thursdays, her mother drives her to school. Write a fraction and shade the model shown to show how many days a week she rides the bus.

_____

2. Christine has 12 cookies to share with her 6 friends. If she gives each friend an equal number of cookies, how many cookies will each friend get? Write a division sentence to show your answer.

_____

3. Tony drew the number line shown and says it represents the fraction $\frac{2}{4}$. Is Tony correct? Explain why or why not.

_____
_____
_____

4. Andreas baked 2 small loaves of cinnamon raisin bread, each with 10 slices. He used 4 slices from each loaf to make toast. Write a fraction to show how many slices of bread Andreas used. Then make a shaded model.

5. Each day, Paul has 4 hours of free time after school. On Monday and Wednesday, he watches television for one hour. On Tuesday and Thursday, he doesn't watch television. On Friday he watches television for two hours. Write fractions to show how much of Paul's free time each day is used for watching television.

_____
_____

6. The table below shows the amount of time Tiffany spends on different after school activities each week. She spends 8 hours on activities in all. Write a fraction to show how much of her activity time Tiffany spends at her music lessons.

Tiffany's After School Activities		
Day	**Activity**	**Hours**
Monday	music lesson	1
Tuesday	scout meeting	$1\frac{1}{2}$
Wednesday	music lesson	2
Thursday	science club	1
Friday	softball practice	$2\frac{1}{2}$

Fractions and Mixed Numbers

CA Standards
KEY NS 1.5, MR 2.6

Improper fractions and Mixed Numbers

Divide to change an improper fraction to a mixed number.	Multiply and add to change a mixed number to an improper fraction.
$\frac{9}{4} = 4\overline{)9}$ $\frac{-8}{1}$ with quotient 2 So $\frac{9}{4} = 2\frac{1}{4}$	$2\frac{1}{4} = \frac{(4 \times 2) + 1}{4} = \frac{9}{4}$ So $2\frac{1}{4} = \frac{9}{4}$

Study this number line. Write each missing fraction.

1.

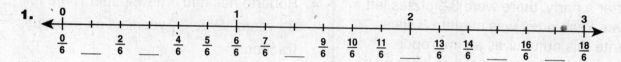

_____

Write each improper fraction as a mixed number or a whole number.

2. $\frac{15}{4}$ **3.** $\frac{19}{5}$ **4.** $\frac{21}{7}$ **5.** $\frac{20}{9}$

_____   _____   _____   _____

Write each mixed number as an improper fraction.

6. $1\frac{4}{5}$ **7.** $3\frac{1}{3}$ **8.** $5\frac{5}{6}$ **9.** $2\frac{7}{8}$

_____   _____   _____   _____

Spiral Review (Chapter 1, Lesson 4) **KEY** NS 1.4, MR 2.3

Find the prime factorization for each number. Use exponents.

10. 72 _____   **11.** 90 _____   **12.** 23 _____

13. Write the prime factorization of 96 in two ways.

_____

Fractions and Mixed Numbers

CA Standards
KEY NS 1.5, MR 2.6

Solve problems 1–6.

1. Lucinda bought 21 sodas for a class party. The sodas come in 6-packs. Write the number of 6-packs that Lucinda has as a mixed number.

   $\frac{21}{6} = 21 \div 6$

2. Ben placed 13 pictures in a photo album. Each page can hold 4 pictures. How many pages can Ben fill in the photo album? Write your answer as an improper fraction.

3. After a party, there were $3\frac{5}{8}$ pizzas left over. Each pizza was cut into 8 slices. Write this number as an improper fraction. How many slices of pizza were left?

4. Roberto has had a newspaper route for $3\frac{3}{4}$ years. Write $3\frac{3}{4}$ years as an improper fraction.

5. Dwayne lent his sister $16\frac{4}{5}$ of a dollar. How much money did Dwayne lend his sister?

6. Do $\frac{38}{5}$ and $8\frac{3}{5}$ represent the same fraction? Explain.

Name _____ Date _____

Equivalent Fractions and Simplest Form

CA Standards
KEY NS 2.3, **KEY** NS 1.5

To find equivalent fractions		
Multiply the numerator and denominator by the same number. $\overset{\times 3}{\frac{3}{8}} = \frac{9}{24}\underset{\times 3}{}$	Divide the numerator and denominator by a common factor. $\overset{\div 2}{\frac{12}{18}} = \frac{6}{9}\underset{\div 2}{}$	Simplest form: Divide numerator and denominator by greatest common factor (GCF). $\overset{\div 6}{\frac{12}{18}} = \frac{2}{3}\underset{\div 6}{}$

Complete.

1. $\frac{5}{8} = \frac{10}{\square}$

2. $\frac{12}{15} = \frac{\square}{5}$

3. $\frac{9}{18} = \frac{1}{\square}$

4. $\frac{2}{3} = \frac{\square}{9}$

5. $\frac{7}{10} = \frac{\square}{100}$

6. $\frac{21}{27} = \frac{7}{\square}$

7. $\frac{6}{30} = \frac{3}{\square}$

8. $\frac{10}{25} = \frac{\square}{50}$

Simplify each fraction.

9. $\frac{22}{4}$

10. $\frac{20}{16}$

11. $\frac{22}{32}$

12. $\frac{45}{36}$

13. $\frac{35}{15}$

14. $\frac{42}{48}$

15. $\frac{30}{9}$

16. $\frac{40}{16}$

Spiral Review (Chapter 1, Lesson 4) NS 1.3, **KEY** NS 1.4

Find the prime factorization for each number. Use exponents if possible.

17. 64 _____

18. 81 _____

19. 94 _____

20. How could you find the number with the prime factorization of $2^2 \times 3^2$?

_____

Equivalent Fractions and Simplest Form

CA Standards
KEY NS 2.3, KEY NS 1.5

Solve problems 1–6.

1. Harold has been given this list of equivalent fractions: $\frac{6}{14}, \frac{12}{28}, \frac{3}{7}$. He is supposed to choose the fraction that is in simplest form. Which one should Harold choose?

   _____

2. Mary Lou said that $\frac{16}{20}$ in simplest form is $\frac{8}{10}$. What was her mistake? What is the correct answer?

   _____

   _____

   _____

3. The fifth and sixth grades at Oak Street School are having a science fair. There are 50 students total and $\frac{3}{5}$ of the students are fifth grade students. How many fifth grade students are entered in the science fair?

   _____

   _____

4. A nurse works 2 out of every 3 days. Write fractions to tell how many days she works out of the following total days: 6, 9, 12, 15

   $\frac{2}{3}, \overline{6}, \overline{9}, \overline{12}, \overline{15}$

5. $\frac{7}{8}$ of the animals at a shelter are cats. If there are 400 animals at the shelter, how many are cats?

   _____

6. Trish walks 15 blocks to school. If she walks $\frac{2}{10}$ of the way by herself, how many blocks does she walk by herself? How many blocks does she walk with a friend.

   _____

Compare Fractions

CA Standards
KEY NS 1.5, MR 1.1

Which is greater, $\frac{4}{5}$, or $\frac{5}{6}$?

Way ❶ Use a number line.

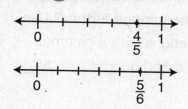

Solution: $\frac{4}{5} < \frac{5}{6}$.

Way ❷ Find a common denominator.

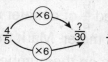

$4 \times 6 = 24$, so $\frac{4}{5} = \frac{24}{30}$.

$5 \times 5 = 25$, so $\frac{5}{6} = \frac{25}{30}$.

**Compare these fractions. Use a number line to help. Write <, >, or =
for each ◯.**

1. $\frac{3}{10}$ ◯ $\frac{4}{7}$ **2.** $\frac{5}{6}$ ◯ $\frac{6}{7}$ **3.** $\frac{3}{9}$ ◯ $\frac{4}{12}$ **4.** $\frac{4}{5}$ ◯ $\frac{3}{4}$ **5.** $\frac{7}{10}$ ◯ $\frac{6}{9}$

**Compare these fractions. Find a common denominator. Write <, >, =
for each ◯.**

6. $\frac{1}{4}$ ◯ $\frac{5}{20}$ **7.** $\frac{5}{8}$ ◯ $\frac{4}{7}$ **8.** $\frac{6}{10}$ ◯ $\frac{9}{12}$ **9.** $\frac{4}{6}$ ◯ $\frac{3}{4}$ **10.** $\frac{12}{28}$ ◯ $\frac{3}{7}$

11. $\frac{2}{5}$ ◯ $\frac{2}{9}$ **12.** $\frac{11}{25}$ ◯ $\frac{24}{50}$ **13.** $\frac{2}{5}$ ◯ $\frac{5}{12}$ **14.** $\frac{6}{11}$ ◯ $\frac{4}{9}$ **15.** $\frac{3}{15}$ ◯ $\frac{2}{10}$

Spiral Review (Chapter 1, Lesson 5) **KEY** NS 1.4, MR 2.4

Find the greatest common factor (GCF) of the numbers.

16. 15, 45 _____   **17.** 12, 28 _____   **18.** 30, 40 _____

19. Nancy wants to plant 16 tulip bulbs and 24 daffodil bulbs. She wants
to plant rows of tulips and rows of daffodils. She wants the same
number of flowers in each row. What are the longest rows of
flowers she can plant?

_____

Name _____ Date _____

Compare Fractions

CA Standards
KEY NS 1.5, MR 1.1

Solve problems 1–6.

1. Dan and Maisie were practicing their long jumps for a track meet. For their first jump, Dan jumped $\frac{7}{8}$ of a meter and Maisie jumped $\frac{5}{6}$ of a meter. Mark the lengths of their jumps on the number lines. Who jumped further?

   Dan ←|—+—+—+—+—+—+—+—|→

   Maisie ←|—+—+—+—+—+—|→

   _____

2. For their second jump, Dan jumped $\frac{8}{10}$ of a meter and Maisie jumped $\frac{6}{7}$ of a meter. Who jumped further? Use equivalent fractions with a common denominator to find out.

   $\frac{8}{10} = \frac{}{70}$

   $\frac{6}{7} = \frac{}{70}$

   _____

3. Sebastian and Ellie each have a bag with the same number of marbles. Sebastian took out $\frac{2}{5}$ of his marbles for a game. Ellie took out $\frac{5}{7}$ of her marbles. Who took out more marbles?

   _____

4. Max and Henry were picking tomatoes in their garden. Max picked $\frac{1}{4}$ of the tomatoes and Henry picked $\frac{2}{3}$ of the tomatoes. Who picked the most tomatoes?

   _____

5. Victoria, Sean, and Maura were picking apples at a farm. Victoria picked $\frac{3}{5}$ of a basket, Sean picked $\frac{3}{4}$ of a basket, and Maura picked $\frac{1}{5}$ of a basket. Write the names of the people who picked apples in order from the greatest amount picked to the least amount picked.

   _____

6. Raul surveyed his class about sports. $\frac{5}{12}$ of the students like baseball, $\frac{7}{10}$ of the students like soccer, and $\frac{7}{8}$ of the students like football. Which sport was liked by the most students? Explain how you know.

   _____

   _____

   _____

Problem Solving: Compare Data Sets

The table shows the number of peanut and popcorn bags sold at the zoo concession stand in one week. Which snack had a greater fraction sold on Saturday?

Snack	Number of Bags Sold in One Week	Number of Bags Sold on Saturday
peanuts	40	10
popcorn	60	20

10 out of 40 bags of peanuts

$$\frac{10}{40} = \frac{1}{4}$$

20 out of 60 bags of popcorn

$$\frac{20}{60} = \frac{1}{3}$$

Since $\frac{1}{3}$ is greater than $\frac{1}{4}$, the bags of popcorn had a greater fraction sold on Saturday.

Solve. Explain why your answer makes sense.

1. The snack shop sold 50 hamburgers and 75 cheeseburgers last week, 25 of each were sold on Thursday. Which had a greater fraction sold on Thursday?

_____

2. The snack shop sold 40 popsicles on Monday and 25 on Tuesday. On Monday 10 of the popsicles sold were orange and on Tuesday 5 of the popsicles sold were orange. Which day had the greatest fraction of orange popsicles?

_____

_____

Spiral Review (Chapter 2, Lesson 4) **KEY NS 1.5, MR 1.1**

Compare. Write <, >, or = for each ◯.

3. $\frac{2}{9}$ ◯ $\frac{3}{4}$

4. $\frac{4}{12}$ ◯ $\frac{2}{6}$

5. Janice asked visitors at the zoo about their favorite animal. One third of the people chose giraffes. Three sixths of the people chose lions. Which animal was chosen by more people?

_____

Problem Solving: Compare Data Sets

CA Standard
MR 1.2, SDAP 1.3

Solve. Explain why your answers make sense.

1. In the Reptile House, Kendra counted 2 out of 4 lizards that had dark green stripes and 5 out of 8 snakes that had dark green stripes. Which reptile had a greater fraction of dark green stripes?

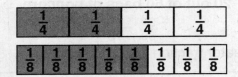

2. One third of the hippos were in the water in the morning and four sixths of the hippos were in the water in the afternoon. At which time was the greatest fraction of the hippos in the water?

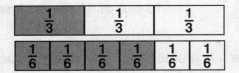

3. A male prairie dog ate 8 out of 12 pounds of food and a female prairie dog ate 4 out of 5 pounds of food. Which prairie dog ate the greatest fractional amount of food?

4. Rita spent $25 at the zoo and Sean spent $20. At the gift shop, Rita spent $15 and Sean spent $10. Who spent the greatest fraction of money at the gift shop?

5. Kate has 90 stickers in her sticker collection. Of those stickers 36 are bird stickers, 9 are mammal stickers, and the rest are reptile stickers. How many reptile stickers are in her collection? What fraction of her collection are reptile stickers?

6. The python snake climbed 10 feet up a 12 foot tree and the boa constrictor snake climbed 16 feet up an 18 foot tree. Write the fraction of the tree each snake climbed. Simplify the fractions and compare the distances.

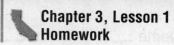
Hands On: Represent Whole Numbers and Decimals

CA Standard
NS 1.1

Decimal Notation	Fraction Notation	Word Form	Model with Bills and Coins	Money Amount
5.6	$5\frac{6}{10}$	five and six tenths		$5.60
12.75	$12\frac{75}{100}$	twelve and seventy-five hundredths		$12.75

Write the word form as a money amount.

1. six and thirty-five hundredths

_____

2. seventeen and four tenths

_____

3. ten and ninety-nine thousandths

_____

Model each number using money. Use the fewest number of bills and coins.

4. 3.05

_____

_____

5. 10.70

_____

_____

6. 16.32

_____

_____

Spiral Review (Chapter 1, Lesson 4) **KEY NS 1.4**

Write the prime factorization of each number using exponents.

7. 15 _____

8. 60 _____

9. 28 _____

10. 49 _____

11. Ian says that the prime factorization of 12 is 3 × 4. Is he correct? Explain.

_____

_____

Name _____ Date _____

Hands On: Represent Whole Numbers and Decimals

CA Standard
NS 1.1

Solve Problems 1–6.

1. Jessica's lunch cost $4.89. What is the value of the digit in the tenths place?

_____

2. What is the least amount of bills that could be used to make $12? The most?

_____

_____

3. What is the value of the bills and coins using whole numbers and decimals?

4. If Sara gave the cashier ten and thirty-four hundredths, how much money did the cashier receive?

_____

5. Mr. Harris bought a basketball for $18 \frac{3}{10}$ dollars. He gave the cashier a $20 bill. How much money did he receive as change?

_____

_____

6. Briana bought a bag of popcorn for two and fifty-five hundredths dollars. Marissa bought a soda for $1 \frac{89}{100}$ dollars. Kim spent 2.05 dollars on a box of candy. Who spent the most amount of money? How much did she spend?

_____

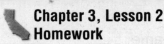

Place Value Through Billions

CA Standards
NS 1.0, NS 1.3

	You can write numbers in different ways. 312,501 can be written in:
Standard From	Use digits—312,501
Word Form	Use words–three hundred twelve thousand, five hundred one
Short Word Form	Use digits and words–312 thousand, 501
Expanded Form	Use digits to show the value of each place 300,000 + 10,000 + 2,000 + 500 + 1 = (3 × 100,000) + (1 × 10,000) + (2 × 1,000) + (5 × 100) + (1 × 1)

Write each number in standard form.

1. 415 thousand, 25

2. 800,000 + 4,000 + 60 + 2

3. 100,000 + 900 + 20 + 3

_____

_____

_____

Write each number in expanded form using exponents.

4. 702,946

_____

5. 8,325

_____

6. At times, the earth is two hundred thirty-eight thousand, eight hundred fifty-seven miles from the moon. Write this number is standard form.

_____

Spiral Review (Chapter 1, Lesson 4) NS 1.3, **KEY** NS 1.4

Write the prime factorization of each number using exponents.

7. 24 _____   **8.** 32 _____   **9.** 45 _____   **10.** 54 _____

11. The area of a square is 7 × 7 square inches. Write this using an exponent.

_____

Place Value Through Billions

CA Standards
NS 1.0, NS 1.3

Solve problems 1–6.

1. What is the value of the 5 in the number 285,467?

Thousands			Ones		
hundreds	tens	ones	hundreds	tens	ones
			,		

_____

2. A family bought a new van that costs twenty-two thousand, five hundred thirty-five dollars. How can the number be written in standard form?

_____

3. The table shows the most popular female names. Identify the most popular name and write the number in word form.

Female Names	
Name	**Number of People**
Patricia	153,834
Mary	376,915
Linda	148,386

_____

_____

4. Suppose 100 more females had the name Linda. How many would that be?

_____

5. The toy drive raised $25,460 in toys and the food drive raised $17,350 in food. Write the total amount of money raised in expanded form using exponents.

_____

_____

6. In August, the post office delivers 785,329 pieces of mail to customers. In December, the post office delivers 9,347,089 pieces of mail to customers. Write the difference between the two months in standard form and word form.

_____

_____

_____

Place Value Through Thousandths

CA Standard
NS 1.0

Place Value Chart

62.8<u>3</u>5

The value of the underlined

digit is three hundredths.

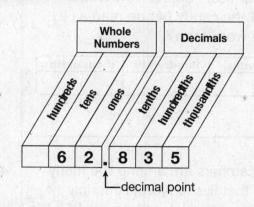

—decimal point

Write each decimal in standard form.

1. twelve and fifty-four hundredths _____   **2.** six and sixteen thousandths _____

3. one hundred sixty-two thousandths _____   **4.** twenty and five hundredths _____

Write each decimal in word form.

5. 23.6

_____

6. 8.002

_____

7. 10.01

_____

8. 2.112

_____

Spiral Review (Chapter 3, Lesson 2) **NS 1.0, NS 1.3**

Write each number in standard form.

9. 40,000 + 5,000 + 40 + 2 _____

10. 100,000 + 3,000 + 500 + 70 + 9 _____

11. The water at Yosemite Falls descends 2,425 feet. Write this number in expanded form.

_____

Place Value Through Thousandths

Solve problems 1–6.

1. A candy bar costs $0.67. How would the cost of the candy bar be read as a decimal in word form?

ones		tenths	hundredths	thousandths
	.			

_____

2. A recipe needs three and two tenths of a cup of milk. Write the amount of milk needed in standard form.

_____

3. Tyrant Flycatchers are among the many songbirds that live in North America. Flycatchers may weigh as little as 4.5 grams. Write this weight in word form.

_____

_____

4. A Sand Martin makes its nest at the end of a 0.75 meter tunnel. Draw and shade a decimal square to represent 0.75.

_____

5. Alex said the decimal 2.340 is read two and thirty four tenths. Marcus said Alex was wrong and the decimal is read two and three hundred forty thousandths. Who is correct? Explain why.

_____

_____

_____

6. Jason ran the 40-yard dash 0.45 seconds faster than Michael. Michael ran the race in 5.75 seconds. Alex ran the race 0.05 seconds slower than Michael. Write each boy's time. Who finished first, second, and third?

_____

_____

_____

_____

Compare and Order Whole Numbers and Decimals

Compare 6,490,232,908 and 6,495,590,028

Step 1 Write the numbers in a vertical list. Line up the numbers by place value.

6,490,232,908
6,495,590,028

Step 2 Start from the left. Compare the digits.

6,490,232,908
6,495,590,028

The millions place is different. 5 is greater than 0.
Solution: 6,495,590,028 > 6,490,232,908

Compare. Write >, <, or = for each ◯.

1. 24,981 ◯ 24,810

2. 734,556 ◯ 734,655

3. 45,813,540 ◯ 48,513,450

4. 2,198,070 ◯ 2,189,007

Order each set of numbers from greatest to least.

5. 9,254; 9,542; 9,515

6. 18,229; 18,209; 18,299

7. A toy company had a profit of $259,304 this year and $254,509 last year. Which profit was greater? Explain.

Spiral Review (Chapter 2, Lesson 2) **KEY** NS 1.5, MR 2.6

Write each improper fraction as a mixed number or a whole number.

8. $\frac{5}{4}$ _____

9. $\frac{8}{5}$ _____

10. At the bake sale, pies were cut into 8 pieces and sold by the slice. At the end of the sale, there were 11 pieces left. How much pie is left? Write your answer in different ways.

Name _____ Date _____

Compare and Order Whole Numbers and Decimals

CA Standards
NS 1.0, MR 2.0

Solve problems 1-6.

1. Tyra ran a race in 8.45 minutes, Heather ran in 8.52 minutes, and Marie ran in 8.50 minutes. Order their times from least to greatest. Who ran the race in the fastest time?

   _____

2. The Myers family is going to buy a new house. The first house they look at costs $560,389, and the second house they look at costs $506,392. Compare the prices of the houses using <, >, or =.

   _____

3. There are about 4,183,898 people in Michigan that use the Internet. There are about 4,620,671 people in Ohio that use the Internet. Compare the number of people in each state that use the internet using <, >, or =.

   _____

4. On Monday night, Jack finished his homework in 30.45 minutes. On Tuesday night, Jack finished his homework in 33.2 minutes. On Wednesday night, Jack finished his homework in 30.4 minutes. Order the times from least to greatest.

   _____

5. The amusement park sold 234,560 hot dogs and 219,450 bags of popcorn last year. This year, they sold 244,675 hot dogs and 207,480 bags of popcorn. Compare the total number of hot dogs and bags of popcorn sold each year.

   _____

6. Greg's relay team members ran a race in 3.15 minutes, 3.22 minutes, 3.45 minutes, and 3.05 minutes. Ryan's relay team members ran the same race in 3.07 minutes, 3.40 minutes, 3.25 minutes, and 3.29 minutes. What were the total times for each team? Compare to find which team had the fastest time.

   _____

   _____

   _____

   _____

Round Whole Numbers and Decimals

Round 0.3<u>2</u>6 to the place indicated by the underlined digit.

Step 1 Circle the digit to the right of the underlined digit.

0.3②6

Step 2 If the circled digit is 5 or greater, increase the rounding place digit by 1. If the digit is less than 5, do not change the rounding place digit. Drop all remaining digits after rounding.

Solution: 0.3<u>2</u>6 rounds to 0.3.

Round to the place indicated by the underlined digit.

1. 7.1<u>5</u>6 _____

2. 34.<u>2</u>77 _____

3. 0.<u>9</u>81 _____

4. 10.<u>9</u>1 _____

5. 17.1<u>5</u>6 _____

6. 0.2<u>8</u>8 _____

7. 46<u>2</u>,969 _____

8. 1,9<u>0</u>6,230,234 _____

9. <u>2</u>39,796 _____

10. 6.<u>0</u>3 _____

11. 28,3<u>3</u>4 _____

12. <u>4</u>8.290 _____

Spiral Review (Chapter 2, Lesson 3) **KEY** NS 2.3, **KEY** NS 1.5

Write each fraction in simplest form.

13. $\frac{4}{6}$ _____

14. $\frac{2}{8}$ _____

15. 16 out of 20 students are riding the bus. Write the fraction of students that are riding the bus in simplest form.

_____

Round Whole Numbers and Decimals

CA Standards
NS 1.1, MR 1.0

Solve problems 1–6.

1. A house costs $195,500. Round the amount to the nearest hundred thousand.

   $<u>1</u>95,500

   _____

2. Karen rounded $14.58 to $14.00. Explain why her answer is incorrect.

   _____

   _____

   _____

3. Use data from the table to solve Problems 3–4.

2006 Middlesex County High Schools Top Five Hitters		
Player	**Team**	**Average**
Javier Ordonez	Tigers	0.320
Junior Ramirez	Griffons	0.349
Kazuya Suzuki	Eagles	0.321
Mark Sweeney	Mustangs	0.340
Tony Williams	Panthers	0.333

   Round Javier Ordonez's average to the nearest tenth.

   _____

4. Round all of the averages to the nearest hundredth. Who had the best batting average?

   _____

   _____

   _____

5. Lacey needs to buy two presents for her sister. The first present costs $29.57 and the second present costs $5.19. About how much did Lacey spend on both presents?

   _____

6. A train traveled 32,190 miles round trip last week and 32,830 miles this week. If you round each distance to the nearest ten thousand, can you determine which week the train traveled the farthest?

   _____

Problem Solving: Estimate or Exact?

CA Standards
MR 2.5, NS 1.1

Solve. Explain why you used an estimate or an exact answer.

Example 1: Need an exact answer	Example 2: Need an estimate	Population of the 5 Largest Cities in California (2000)	
How many more people live in San Francisco compared to Long Beach? Find the difference.	About how many more people live in San Diego compared to San Jose? Use rounding rules.	**City**	**Population**
		Los Angeles	3,694,820
$\begin{array}{r} 776{,}733 \\ -\ 461{,}522 \\ \hline 315{,}211 \text{ people} \end{array}$	$\begin{array}{r} 1{,}223{,}400 \quad 1{,}200{,}000 \\ 894{,}943\ -\ 900{,}000 \\ \hline 300{,}000 \\ \text{people} \end{array}$	San Diego	1,223,400
		San Jose	894,943
		San Francisco	776,733
		Long Beach	461,522

Use the table below to solve.

1. What is the difference in voter turnout from 2000 to 2002?

_____

_____

2. About how many more people voted in 2004 than in 1996?

_____

_____

National Voter Turnout in Federal Elections	
Year	**Voter Turnout**
2004	122,294,978
2002	79,830,119
2000	105,586,274
1998	73,117,022
1996	96,456,345

Spiral Review (Chapter 2, Lesson 3) **KEY NS 2.3**

Write each fraction in simplest form.

3. $\frac{3}{30}$ _____

4. $\frac{2}{8}$ _____

5. Jenny says that $\frac{5}{10}$ of her stuffed animals are bears. What is $\frac{5}{10}$ in simplest form? _____

Problem Solving: Estimate or Exact?

Use the tables to solve. Explain why you used an estimate or an exact answer.

Mountains in the US higher than 14,000 feet	
Mountain	Height
Mt. McKinley	20,320
Mt. St. Elias	18,008
Mt. Foraker	17,400
Mt. Bona	16,500
Mt. Blackburn	16,390

Public Higher Education Costs, 2000–2005	
Year	Cost
2000–2001	$7,586
2001–2002	$8,022
2002–2003	$8,502
2003–2004	$9,249
2004–2005	$9,877

For 1–4, use the Mountains in the US Higher Than 14,000 Feet table to solve.

1. How much higher is Mt. St. Elias than Mt. Bona?

   _____

   $18,008 - 16,500 =$ _____ .

2. Which two mountain peaks have a difference of about 2,000 ft? Round your answer to the nearest thousand.

   _____

   _____

   _____

3. How much shorter is Mt. Blackburn than Mt. McKinley?

   _____

   _____

   _____

4. If you stacked Mt. Foraker, Mt. Bona, and Mt. Blackburn on top of each other, about how tall would they be? Round your answer to the nearest thousand.

   _____

   _____

For 5–6, use the Public Higher Education Costs table.

5. Jason started college during the 2001-2002 school year and graduated during the 2004-2005 school year. How much money did Jason's education cost?

   _____

   _____

   _____

6. A private college education costs about twice as much as a public college education. About how much would Jason have spent in 2001-2002 if he'd gone to a private college?

   _____

   _____

   _____

Hands On: Fractions and Decimals

CA Standards
KEY NS 1.5, MR 2.3

Use number lines to find the decimal equivalent of a fraction.

What is the decimal equivalent of $\frac{2}{5}$?

Step 1 Use the decimal number line and the number line marked in fifths.

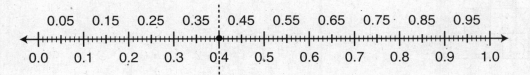

Step 2 At the point of $\frac{2}{5}$, place a ruler vertically so it crosses the decimal number line and identify 0.4 as the decimal the line goes through.

Use the number line. Write each fraction as a decimal.

1. $\frac{1}{5}$

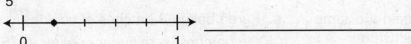
_____

2. $\frac{5}{10}$

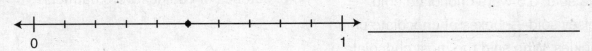
_____

Spiral Review (Chapter 3, Lesson 2) **NS 1.0, NS 1.3**

Identify the place value of the underlined number.

3. 12,347 _____   **4.** 263,530 _____

5. The paper Sue wrote for English class has a total of 234,879 letters, numbers and other characters. Identify the place value of the underlined number.

_____

Use with text pp. 76–77

Hands On: Fractions and Decimals

CA Standards
KEY NS 1.5, MR 2.3

Solve.

1. Brody built a tower out of blocks. Write a fraction and decimal that represents the number of white blocks.

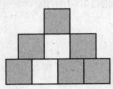

_____ = _____
Fraction   Decimal

2. The fraction $\frac{6}{10}$ is not written in simplest form. Write the fraction in simplest form and the equivalent decimal.

_____ = _____
Fraction   Decimal

3. Miles started with 10 brownies each day to sell at a bake sale. He sold $\frac{3}{4}$ of the brownies on Saturday and 0.8 of the brownies on Sunday. On which day did he sell more brownies?

_____

4. A recipe called for $\frac{1}{4}$ cup sugar and 0.2 cup of butter. Did the recipe call for more sugar or butter?

_____

5. Maria, Kelsey, and Rita all sold the same number of boxes of cookies. Of the boxes of cookies Maria sold, $\frac{3}{5}$ were chocolate chip. Of the boxes of cookies Rita sold, 0.5 were chocolate chip. Kelsey sold $\frac{2}{10}$ boxes of chocolate chip cookies. Who sold the most chocolate chip cookies? Explain.

_____

_____

_____

6. Karen baked 8 batches of cookies. $\frac{1}{2}$ of the batches were sugar cookies. 0.25 of the batches were chocolate chip. The other batches were oatmeal. How many batches of cookies were oatmeal?

_____

_____

_____

Equivalent Fractions and Decimals

CA Standard
MR 2.3

Write fractions and mixed numbers as decimals.

HINT: Make the denominator a multiple of ten.

$$\overset{\times 2}{\underset{\times 2}{\text{Fraction: } \frac{4}{5} = \frac{8}{10} = 0.8}}$$

$$\overset{\times 25}{\underset{\times 25}{\text{Mixed Number: } 2\frac{3}{4} = 2\frac{75}{100} = 2.75}}$$

Write a decimal as a fraction or mixed number in simplest form.

Decimal less than 1 (fraction):

$$\overset{\div 2}{\underset{\div 2}{0.4 = \frac{4}{10} = \frac{2}{5}}}$$

Decimal greater than 1 (mixed number):

$$\overset{\div 2}{\underset{\div 2}{1.6 = 1\frac{6}{10} = 1\frac{3}{5}}}$$

Write each decimal as a fraction or mixed number in simplest form.

1. 0.75 _____

2. 1.5

3. 2.25

4. 1.6

Write each fraction or mixed number as a decimal.

5. $\frac{3}{5}$

6. $\frac{2}{8}$

7. $\frac{14}{20}$

8. $1\frac{3}{10}$

9. $1\frac{4}{8}$

10. $2\frac{2}{20}$

11. $1\frac{4}{5}$

12. $3\frac{1}{4}$

Spiral Review (Chapter 2, Lesson 2) **KEY NS 1.5, MR 2.6**

Write each improper fraction as a mixed number or a whole number.

13. $\frac{7}{5}$

14. $\frac{12}{10}$

15. There are 48 apple slices in the fruit salad that Ben's dad prepared for dinner. The slices were cut from apples that were sliced into 7 pieces each. That means that there were $\frac{48}{7}$ apples used. How many apples were used in the salad? Express the answer as a mixed number.

Equivalent Fractions and Decimals

Solve.

1. Mason lives 4.2 miles from school. He says that is equivalent to $4\frac{1}{5}$ miles. Explain whether Mason is correct.

   _____

   _____

   _____

2. The playground is $2\frac{3}{4}$ miles from Jason's house. The library is 2.25 miles from his house. Is the playground or library closer to Jason's house?

   _____

   _____

3. Complete the chart below by finding the equivalent distances. Record the mixed numbers in simplest form.

Highest Score			
Distance	Fraction	=	Decimal
Sack Race		=	9.25 yards
Ballon Toss	$8\frac{3}{4}$ feet	=	
Egg Race		=	5.4 feet

4. Drake's relay team finished the race in $5\frac{3}{4}$ minutes. Kevin's relay team finished in 5.4 minutes. Whose team ran the relay in a faster time?

   _____

5. Evan ran 2.5 miles on Saturday and 2.25 miles on Sunday. Alex ran $2\frac{2}{5}$ miles on Saturday and $2\frac{1}{2}$ miles on Sunday. Who ran a total of more miles?

   _____

   _____

   _____

6. Wes and his father rode their bikes three weekends in a row. They rode $5\frac{1}{4}$ miles during the first weekend, $5\frac{1}{2}$ miles during the second weekend, and 5.75 miles during the third weekend. What is the mean number of miles that Wes and his father rode?

   _____

   _____

Compare and Order Fractions and Decimals

CA Standard
KEY NS 1.5

Different Ways to Compare 2.4, $2\frac{1}{4}$, and 2.04	
Way 1: Write the mixed number as a decimal. $2\frac{1}{4} = 2.25$ Compare the decimals. $2.04 < 2.25 < 2.4$	**Way 2:** Write the decimals as mixed numbers. $2.4 = 2\frac{4}{10}$ $2.04 = 2\frac{4}{100}$ Rename with a common denominator. $2\frac{4}{10} = 2\frac{40}{100}$ $2\frac{1}{4} = 2\frac{25}{100}$ Compare the mixed numbers. $2\frac{4}{100} < 2\frac{25}{100} < 2\frac{40}{100}$

Compare. Write >, <, or = for each $\bigcirc$.

1. $0.6 \bigcirc \frac{1}{5}$ **2.** $9.08 \bigcirc 9\frac{1}{5}$ **3.** $\frac{4}{5} \bigcirc 0.9$ **4.** $1\frac{7}{10} \bigcirc 1.07$

5. $2.5 \bigcirc 2\frac{1}{2}$ **6.** $1\frac{13}{20} \bigcirc 1.8$ **7.** $3.6 \bigcirc 3\frac{6}{100}$ **8.** $\frac{9}{25} \bigcirc 0.4$

Order each set of numbers from least to greatest.

9. $\frac{1}{2}, \frac{6}{10}, 0.2, 0.4$

10. $\frac{3}{10}, 0.75, 1.2, 1\frac{1}{10}$

_____   _____

Spiral Review (Chapter 3, Lesson 2) NS 1.0

Write the numbers in standard form.

11. four hundred thirty two thousandths _____

12. twenty five thousandths _____

13. Cathy's mother teaches 5th grade math and, as a joke, wrote her friend a note saying, "Congratulations! You're $(4 \times 10^5) + (2 \times 10^4) + (8 \times 10^3) + (5 \times 10^2)$ hours old." How many hours old is the friend in standard form?

_____

Compare and Order Fractions and Decimals

CA Standard
KEY NS 1.5

Sovle.

1. Jim ate $\frac{3}{8}$ of a pie and Jung ate 0.25 of the same pie. Shade the amount that Jim and Jung ate. Who ate more pie?

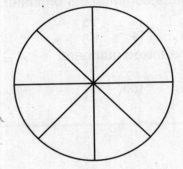

_____

2. Carrie sold $2\frac{3}{5}$ boxes of candy bars. Mollie sold 2.4 boxes of candy bars. Shade the amount that each sold below. Who sold more candy bars?

Carrie

Mollie

_____

3. Marco is 5.5 feet tall, Steve is $5\frac{5}{8}$ feet tall, and Susan is $5\frac{2}{5}$ feet tall. Order the students from shortest to tallest.

_____

4. The students in Mrs. Gumb's class are selling candy bars for a class trip. Each student received the same number to sell. Tina has sold $\frac{2}{3}$ of her candy bars and Chelsea has sold 0.7 of hers. Who has sold more candy bars?

_____

_____

5. Louis caught four fish on his fishing trip. The fish measured $7\frac{1}{4}$ inches, 6.5 inches, $7\frac{1}{2}$ inches, and 7.75 inches. What was the average length of the fish he caught?

_____

6. The aquarium sells fish tanks that hold $12\frac{3}{4}$ gallons, 10.5 gallons, and $8\frac{1}{4}$ gallons of water. What is the average number of gallons that the fish tanks hold?

_____

Mental Math: Fraction and Decimal Equivalents

Visualizing a number line can help to compare and order decimals and fractions.

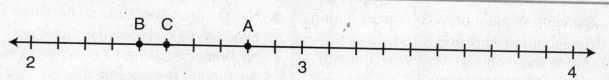

Plot the points on the number line.	Compare the fractions using >, < or =.	Order the fractions from least to greatest.
A $2\frac{8}{10}$ **B** $2\frac{2}{5}$ **C** $2\frac{1}{2}$	$2\frac{8}{10} > 2\frac{1}{2} > 2\frac{2}{5}$	$2\frac{2}{5}, 2\frac{1}{2}, 2\frac{8}{10}$

Dan has to compare fractional and decimal numbers that are in different forms. Compare each pair of numbers and write >, <, or = for each ⬭. Use mental math.

1. $\frac{2}{5}$ ⬭ 0.3   **2.** $1\frac{1}{4}$ ⬭ 1.3   **3.** $4\frac{4}{8}$ ⬭ 4.75   **4.** $4\frac{1}{5}$ ⬭ 4.25

Use the number line to solve.

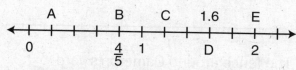

5. Write the fraction and the decimal represented by point *A*.

6. Write the decimal represented by point *B*.

Spiral Review (Chapter 3, Lesson 4) **NS 1.0, MR 2.0**

Compare. Write >, <, or = for each ⬭.

7. 38 ⬭ 37.613   **8.** 7.319 ⬭ 7.367

9. Beth's parents measured her height every six months and marked it in pencil on the wall in her bedroom closet. The last 3 measurements are 58.35 inches, $58\frac{1}{4}$ inches and $58\frac{9}{20}$ inches. Order the numbers from least to greatest.

Use with text pp. 84–85

Name _____ Date _____

Mental Math: Fraction and Decimal Equivalents

CA Standards
KEY NS 1.5, MR 3.3

Sovle problems 1–6.

1. Samantha's plant grew $3\frac{1}{4}$ inches during the month of April and 3.75 inches during the month of May. Which month did the plant grow more?

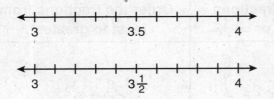

_____

_____

2. Nathan grew two cucumbers. One measured $7\frac{3}{4}$ inches and the other cucumber measured 7.6 inches. What is the greater measurement?

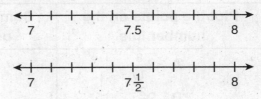

_____

_____

3. Jess bought $1\frac{1}{4}$ pounds of potatoes and 1.3 pounds of onions. Did Jess buy more potatoes or onions?

_____

_____

_____

4. Anita's garden measured 6.4 feet long and $6\frac{2}{5}$ feet wide. What was the shape of her garden? Explain.

_____

_____

_____

5. Frank bought $4\frac{3}{10}$ pounds of apples and 3.5 pounds of tomatoes at a Farmer's Market. His brother bought 2.75 pounds of strawberries and one $5\frac{2}{5}$ pound squash. Who bought more at the Farmer's Market? How many pounds more?

_____

_____

6. The fence around Cameron's yard measures 10.2 feet in length and $5\frac{3}{5}$ feet in width. What is the perimeter of the fence? Draw a picture of the fence and label the length and width. Explain how you found the answer.

_____

_____

_____

Hands On: Algebra and Patterns

CA Standards
KEY AF 1.2, MR 1.1

Jonas made the pattern below using blocks. If the same pattern continues, how many squares would be in Figure 5?

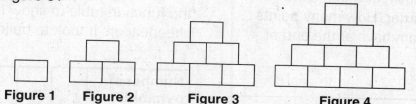

Figure 1   Figure 2   Figure 3   Figure 4

Step 1 Look at how the figure changes each time. Make a table.

Input	Figure Number	1	2	3	4	5
Output	Number of Blocks	1	3	6	10	15

Step 2 Draw and label Figure 5.

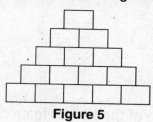

Figure 5

Solution: There will be 15 blocks in Figure 5.

Draw the next figure in the pattern. Describe the rule. Then complete the table.

1. Figure 1   Figure 2   Figure 3

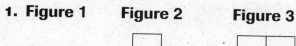

Figure Number	1	2	3	4
Number of Rectangles	3	6	9	

Rule: _____

2. Figure 1 ●●●●●●●●
Figure 2 ●●●●●●
Figure 3 ●●●●

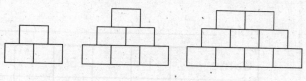

Figure Number	1	2	3	4
Number of Rectangles	8	6	4	

Rule: _____

Spiral Review   (Chapter 2, Lesson 3) **KEY NS 2.3**

Write each fraction in simplest form.

3. $\frac{6}{8}$ _____

4. $\frac{12}{16}$ _____

5. Erin says that $\frac{10}{15}$ of her sweatshirts have cats on them. What is $\frac{10}{15}$ in simplest form? _____

Hands On: Algebra and Patterns

CA Standards
KEY AF 1.2, MR 1.1

Solve problems 1–6.

1. In a football game, the home team scored 1 touchdown and one extra point during every quarter. How many points did the home team have at the end of the game?

_____

2. During halftime at the football game, the cheerleaders built pyramids. Complete the function table to show how many cheerleaders it took to build 5 pyramids.

Number of pyramids	1	2	3	4	5
Number of cheerleaders	3				

_____

_____

3. The coach of the soccer team brought 18 oranges to each game for the players to eat at halftime. Complete the function table to show how many oranges he bought by the end of the season. Then describe the rule.

Rule: _____

Game	1	2	3	4
Number of oranges	18			

4. The number of people attending the school basketball games increased by 15 every game. Complete the table to show the number of people who attended the 5th basketball game. Then describe the rule.

Rule: _____

Game	1	2	3	4	5
Number of people	15				

5. The members of the cross-country team run 5.75 miles every day. Create a function table to show how many miles the members of the cross-country team run in 1 day, 3 days, 7 days, and 10 days. Then describe the rule.

Rule: _____

Days	1	3	7	10
Miles				

6. A student ticket to the football game costs $6.50. Make a function table to show the cost of the tickets if a group buys 3, 5, 7, and 9 student tickets. Then describe the rule.

Rule: _____

Tickets	3	5	7	9
Cost				

Simplify Expressions

CA Standards
KEY AF 1.2, NS 1.3

Simplify this expression using the order of operations.

$$2^3 + 3 \times 4$$

Step 1	**Step 2**	**Step 3**
Simplify the numbers with **exponents**.	**Multiply** from left to right.	**Add** from left to right.
$2^3 + 3 \times 4$ $2 \times 2 \times 2 = 8$	$8 + 3 \times 4$ $8 + 12$	$8 + 12$ 20

Solution: $2^3 + 3 \times 4 = 20$

Simplify.

1. $5 \times (18 - 9)$ ____

2. $(21 - 14) \times (3 + 4)$ ____

3. $(27 - 3^2) - 12$ ____

4. $8 + (52 - 44) - 6$ ____

5. $1 \times (6 + 8) - 2$ ____

6. $(35 - 15) \times (2 + 1)$ ____

7. $(18 - 2^2) + 6$ ____

8. $12 + (13 - 4) + 5$ ____

Spiral Review (Chapter 2, Lesson 3) **KEY** NS 2.3

Write each fraction in simplest form.

9. $\frac{6}{10}$ ____

10. $\frac{15}{20}$ ____

11. Mrs. Jones surveyed the students in her science class about their favorite food. Out of 30 students, 12 voted for Italian food. What is $\frac{12}{30}$ in simplest form? ____

Simplify Expressions

CA Standards
KEY AF 1.2, NS 1.3

Simplify.

1. Which operation should be performed first? Use the order of operations to simplify this expression.

$$3 \times (5 + 4)$$

_____

_____

2. Cole earned $5 an hour for cleaning his room. It took him two hours to clean his room. If his mother paid him for cleaning his room, and gave him an additional $8, how much money does Cole have now?

$$(\$5 \times 2) + \$8$$

_____

_____

3. During basketball practice, one student made 4 baskets. Five other students made 3 baskets each. Another student made 5 baskets. The coach calculated the total number of points made by all of the students. Write an equation to find how many baskets were made in all.

_____

_____

4. Gregory earned $8 each of the 3 times he mowed his neighbors grass, $10 for walking their dog, and $3 each time he watered their plants for 3 days in a row. How much money did Gregory make in all? Write an equation and solve.

_____

_____

5. Mr. Jenkins incorrectly solved this expression. Tell what he did wrong and give the correct answer. Show your work.

$$8 + 2^2 \times 3 - 10$$
$$8 + 4 = 12$$
$$12 \times 3 = 36$$
$$36 - 10 = 26$$

_____

_____

_____

6. Bradley found the value of this expression. Is his answer correct? If not, tell what he did wrong and give the correct answer.

$$36 - 3^2 \times (2 + 1)$$
$$36 - 9 = 25$$
$$25 \times 3 = 75$$

_____

_____

_____

Name _____   Date _____

Write and Evaluate Expressions

CA Standards
KEY AF 1.2, AF 1.0

Derek performed an experiment for his science fair project by drawing the conclusion that for every 1 tablespoon of fertilizer used, the bean plant grew an additional 5 inches. How many inches did the plant grow that was given 6 tablespoons of fertilizer?

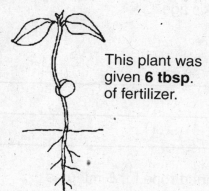

This plant was given **6 tbsp**. of fertilizer.

The bean plant grew **30 inches.**

Step ①	Let f stand for the number of tablespoons of fertilizer.	Choose any letter or symbol for the variable.
Step ②	Then express the number of inches as $5 \times f$ or $5 \cdot f$ or $5f$	You read all these expressions as "5 times *f*".
Step ③	$5f$ 5×6 30	Simplify the expression.

Solution: The bean plant that was given 6 tablespoons of fertilizer grew 30 inches.

Write an algebraic expression for each word phrase.
Use the variable *n* to represent the unknown number.

1. Four times a number plus eight.

_____

2. Five less than a number squared.

_____

3. Nine times a number divided by three.

_____

4. Eight times a number plus seven

_____

Evaluate each expression when $x = 7$ and $d = 9$.

5. $2x + 14$

_____

6. $(5 \times 3) + 5x$

_____

7. $d^2 + 11$

_____

8. $7x - 12$

_____

Spiral Review (Chapter 3, Lesson 5) **NS 1.1**

Round each number to the nearest hundred.

9. 3,678

_____

10. 308,425

_____

11. 47,830.45

_____

12. 104,370.30

_____

Use with text pp. 104–107

Write and Evaluate Expressions

CA Standards
KEY AF 1.2, AF 1.0

Solve problems 1–6.

1. Chad did his homework in 10 minutes on Monday. On Tuesday it took him twice as long to do his homework as it did on Monday. Write an expression to show how long it took Chad to do his homework both nights.

_____

_____

2. Frank is 3 years less than twice as old as Brad. If Brad is 5, write an expression to show Frank's age.

_____

_____

3. Amanda checked out 7 fiction books from the library. She also checked out three times as many non-fiction books. The next day, Amanda returned 5 books to the library. How many books does she have now? Write an expression to explain your answer.

_____

_____

4. Nicole jumped rope for 5 minutes on Monday. On Tuesday she jumped twice as long as she did on Monday. On Wednesday, she jumped 8 minutes longer than she did on Monday. How many minutes did Nicole spend jumping rope all together? Write an expression to explain your answer.

_____

_____

5. Heather is twice as old as Natalie. Abby is 3 years younger than Heather. If Natalie is x years old, how old is Abby? Find Abby's age and Heather's age when $x = 9$. Write expressions to solve. Write the girls' names in order from the oldest to the youngest.

_____

_____

_____

_____

_____

6. Travis wrote the following expression to show that his sister's age is 5 years less than twice his age. Explain what he did wrong. Give the correct expression.

Let a stand for my age.

My sister's age: $a \div 2 - 5$

_____

_____

_____

_____

_____

Write and Solve Equations

CA Standards
KEY AF 1.2, MR 1.1

Use inverse operations to solve equations.

Example 1:	**Example 2:**
Subtraction is the inverse of addition.	Division is the inverse of multiplication.
$x + 12 = 25$	$4x = 36$
$x + 12 - 12 = 25 - 12$	$4x \div 4 = 36 \div 4$
$x + 0 = 13$	$1 \times x = 9$
Solution: $x = 13$	**Solution:** $x = 9$

Solve and check.

1. $r - 45 = 17$ **2.** $44 = 4f$ **3.** $k + 16 = 30$ **4.** $a - 12 = 8$

_____   _____   _____   _____

5. $7y = 42$ **6.** $c - 30 = 27$ **7.** $81 = 9v$ **8.** $b + 15 = 75$

_____   _____   _____   _____

Choose the equation that represents the situation. Then use the equation to solve the problem.

9. Jenni and her friend were having lunch. The bill came to $17. She gave the waiter $21 including tip. How much was the tip?

    A $17 + n = $21   **B** $21 + n = $17

_____

Spiral Review (Chapter 4, Lesson 1) **KEY** NS 1.5

Write each decimal as a fraction. Simplify your answers.

10. 0.25   **11.** 0.6

_____   _____

12. Rebecca's scout troop went camping. Some of the scouts went canoeing and 0.4 of the scouts went horseback riding. Write 0.4 as a fraction. Simplify.

_____

Name _____ Date _____

Write and Solve Equations

CA Standards
KEY AF 1.2, MR 1.1

Solve problems 1–6.

1. Sam spent $14 at the concession stand. His drink cost $3. How much did he spend on other items? Choose the equation that represents the situation. Then use the equation to solve the problem.

    A $14 − $3 = $11

    B $14 + $3 = $17

_____

_____

2. Karen skated around the ice skating rink a total of 10 times. Every two laps took her 1 minute. How many minutes did she skate? Choose the equation that represents the situation. Then use the equation to solve the problem.

    A 10 + 2 = 12 minutes

    B 10 ÷ 2 = 5 minutes

_____

_____

3. Rosie had $20 before she went to the movies. After the movies she had $7. How much money did she spend at the movies? Write an equation and solve.

_____

_____

_____

4. Lianna treated 3 of her friends and herself to ice cream sundaes. The bill for the sundaes was $16. Each sundae cost the same amount. How much did Lianna pay for each sundae? Write an equation and solve.

_____

_____

_____

5. Explain how to find the value of y in the expressions below.

$$5 + y \times 6 = 29$$
$$2y + 12 = 20$$

_____

_____

_____

_____

_____

_____

6. Jess says the square of the sum of 17 plus some number will equal his mother's age squared. If Jess' mother's age squared is 2209, what number must be used to make the equation true?

$$(17 + a)^2 = 2{,}209$$

_____

_____

Variables and Functions

CA Standards
KEY AF 1.5, AF 1.0

Joe made the pattern below out of counters. Look at the pattern. Write the rule. How many squares will there be in Figure 8?

 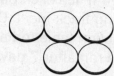  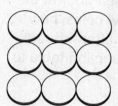

Figure 1   **Figure 2**   **Figure 3**   **Figure 4**

Way 1 Use words.

The number of counters is 2 times the figure number plus one.

Way 2 Use one variable.

x is the input or the figure number.
$2x + 1$ is the output or the number of counters.

Rule: Output = $2x + 1$

Way 3 Use an equation with two variables.

$y = 2x + 1$
$y = (2 \times 8) + 1$
$y = 16 + 1$
$y = 17$

Solution: Figure 8 will have $(2 \times 8) + 1$, or 17 squares.

Use the function table. Read the equation. Then, find the value of y for the given value of x.

1. $y = 14 - x$

x	0	1	2	3
y	___	___	___	___

2. $y = 7x$

x	0	1	2	3
y	___	___	___	___

Spiral Review (Chapter 4, Lesson 3) **KEY** NS 1.5

Compare. Write >, <, or = for each ◯.

3. $\frac{1}{4}$ ◯ 0.5

4. $\frac{2}{3}$ ◯ 0.25

5. Hilda has 1.05 bags of candy. Is 1.05 greater than, less than, or equal to $\frac{1}{2}$? _____

Name _____ Date _____

Variables and Functions

CA Standards
KEY AF 1.5, AF 1.0

Solve problems 1–6.

1. Tyler collects coins. If each hour at the coin show he buys 5 new coins, how many coins will he have after 4 hours? Complete and use the function table to find the answer.

_____

x	1	2	3	4
y	5	10		

2. Jessica ran 4 miles each day to train for her upcoming track meet. Complete and use the function table to find the number of miles she ran after 7 days.

_____

x	1	2	3	4	5	6	7
y	4						

3. Tracy's pay is described by the rule $y = 8x$, where y represents the amount of pay in dollars and x represents the number of hours she worked. How much money does Tracey earn if she works 6 hours? Complete and use the function table to find the answer.

_____

Number of hours worked	1	2	4	6
Pay per hour				

4. Use the function table from Problem 3. If Tracy earned $72, how many hours did she work? Write an equation to prove your answer.

_____

_____

_____

5. A family traveled 175 miles each day of their 5 day vacation. How many more days would they need to travel to have driven over 2,000 miles? How many days would they have to travel in all?

_____

_____

6. Travis earned $214 for each week of work. At the end of the year, Travis's total income was $10,700. How many weeks out of the year, did Travis work? Write an equation to show your answer.

_____

_____

Problem Solving: Write an Expression

CA Standards
KEY AF 1.2, MR 2.4

Write an expression to solve each problem. Simplify.

Fragrant Flowers sells fresh flowers wrapped in bouquets. Each bouquet is $7. If a customer buys 3 bouquets, the owner of the store will discount the total price by $5. How much does it cost to buy 3 bouquets?

Step 1 What operation will I use to solve this problem?	**Step 2** What will my variable represent?	**Step 3** Should I use parentheses in my expression?	**Solution:**
■ "Buys 3 bouquets" indicates multiplication	p for price	Hint: You can write the expression 2 ways.	$(3 \times p) - 5$ $(3 \times \$7) - 5$ $\$21 - 5$ $\$16$
■ "Discount the total price" indicates subtraction		■ $(3 \times p) - 5$ ■ $3p - 5$	

Write an expression to solve each problem. Simplify.

1. Yu Min made brownies for school. After cutting the brownies into equal pieces, Yu Min gave 4 to her brother, and she split the remaining brownies with her mathematics teacher and her art teacher. If she had 24 brownies, how many brownies did each of the two teachers receive?

   _____

2. The force of gravity on the moon is $\frac{1}{6}$ of the earth's gravity. Therefore, an item on the moon will weigh $\frac{1}{6}$ of what that item weighs on earth. If a tool weights 72 pounds on earth, how much does it weigh on the moon?

   _____

Spiral Review (Chapter 4, Lesson 3) **KEY NS 1.5**

Compare. Write >, <, or = for each ◯.

3. $\frac{3}{7}$ ◯ 0.7

4. $\frac{4}{15}$ ◯ 0.12

5. Jamie had $\frac{5}{6}$ of her mathematics quiz correct. On her science quiz she had 0.7 of the questions correct. On which quiz did Jamie receive a better score? _____

Problem Solving: Write an Expression

CA Standards
KEY AF 1.2, MR 2.4

Write an expression to solve each problem.

1. At the Cupcake Factory, Ramon buys one large chocolate cupcake for $2.50 and spends 6 times as much on lemon cupcakes. How much does Ramon spend on cupcakes?

2. To make a pillow, Kira needs 56 inches of fabric and 4 times that amount of trim. How much trim does Kira need?

3. John spent 5 more hours working on his science fair project than Hannah. Abigail spent twice as long as John. If Hannah spent 19 hours on her project, how long did it take Abigail to complete her project?

4. Kevin has a collection of football cards. He has 3 times as many American Conference cards as National Conference cards. He decides to give 32 American Conference cards to his cousin. If he had 46 National Conference cards, how many American Conference cards does he now have?

5. Noreen makes clay pottery. On Saturday, she had 15 pottery vases. On Sunday, she made 5 more, and on Monday, she sold half of the total number of vases. By Wednesday, she had sold 3 more vases, and had made 5 more. How many vases did she have by the end of the day on Wednesday?

6. Make a story problem for the expression below. Then solve the problem.
$(n + 15) \div 5$

Hands On: Model the Distributive Property

CA Standards
AF 1.3, MR 2.3

Use the Distributive Property to multiply 3 × 13.

Step 1 Draw a rectangle that is 3 units wide and 13 units long.

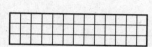

Step 2 Divide the rectangle into two parts.

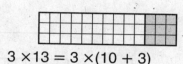

$3 \times 13 = 3 \times (10 + 3)$

Step 3 Use the Distributive Property to find the number of squares in each of the two sections of the rectangle. Then add the partial products.

$(3 \times 10) + (3 \times 3)$

$30 \quad + \quad 9$

39

Use the Distributive Property to multiply. Show the partial products for each and find the sum. Then write a multiplication sentence for each.

1.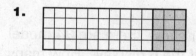

_____

_____

2.

_____

_____

(Chapter 2, Lesson 3) **KEY NS 2.3**

Simplify.

3. $\dfrac{4}{10}$ _____

4. $\dfrac{10}{45}$ _____

5. Mrs. Smith has 8 cupcakes. Six of her cupcakes have frosting. Mrs. Smith wants to represent her cupcakes as a fraction, but $\dfrac{6}{8}$ is too big. Simplify $\dfrac{6}{8}$.

_____

Hands On: Model the Distributive Property

Use rectangles and the Distributive Property to solve problems 1–6.

1. A marching band has 16 rows with 5 band members in each row. How many band members are there in all?

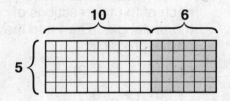

$5 \times 16 = (5 \times 10) + (5 \times 6)$

= _____ + _____

= _____ band members

2. In the Faber School cafeteria, there are 23 students sitting at 6 tables. How many students are at the tables in all?

_____

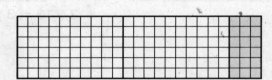

3. There are 4 singers in each of 19 choirs performing at a competition. How many singers are there in all?

_____

_____

_____

4. At a model car show, there are 34 model cars in each of the 6 displays. How many model cars are there in all?

_____

_____

_____

5. Ken deposits $45 each week at his bank. How much has Ken deposited after 3 weeks?

_____

_____

6. There are 114 students in each of the 4 grades in Lincoln High School. How many students are there in Lincoln High School?

_____

_____

_____

Use the Distributive Property

CA Standards
AF 1.3, MR 1.1

Two Ways to Use the Distributive Property to Multiply	
Way 1 $a(b + c) = 6 \times (14 + 18)$ $= 6 \times 32$ $= 192$	**Way 2** $(a \times b) + (a \times c) = (6 \times 14) + (6 \times 18)$ $= 84 + 108$ $= 192$

Use the Distributive Property to find the value of the variable.

1. $3 \times 66 = (j \times 60) + (3 \times 6)$

   _____

2. $8 \times 15 = (8 \times 10) + (8 \times m)$

   _____

3. $y \times 38 = (9 \times 30) + (9 \times 8)$

   _____

4. $4 \times 89 = (4 \times b) + (4 \times 34)$

   _____

5. $6 \times k = (6 \times 42) + (6 \times 12)$

   _____

6. $7 \times 28 = (7 \times 14) + (h \times 14)$

   _____

7. $c \times 42 = (8 \times 21) + (8 \times 21)$

   _____

8. $7 \times 73 = (7 \times b) + (7 \times 18)$

   _____

Spiral Review (Chapter 2, Lesson 3) **KEY NS 2.3**

Simplify.

9. $\frac{16}{40}$ _____

10. $\frac{12}{15}$ _____

11. Jen has 45 flowers in a garden. Twenty of the flowers are red. Jen wants to represent this number as a fraction, but $\frac{20}{45}$ is too big. Simplify $\frac{20}{45}$ for Jen.

   _____

Use the Distributive Property

Use the Distributive Property to solve problems 1–6.

1. Deb puts 7 flowers in one vase and 8 flowers in another vase. Steve puts 6 times the number of Deb's flowers in vases. How many flowers did Steve put into vases? Write two expressions. Then use the expressions to find the answer.

1: $6 \times (8 + 7) = 6 \times$ _____

= _____

2: $(6 \times 7) + (6 \times 8) =$ ____ + 48

= _____

2. Johnny has 12 red buttons and 14 blue buttons. He has 3 times as many marbles as buttons. How many marbles does Johnny have? Write an equation to find out.

_____ × _____ + _____ × _____

= _____ + _____

= _____ marbles

3. Joanne sings for 23 minutes. Cheryl sings for 15 minutes. Gina sings for 2 times as many minutes as Joanne and Cheryl together. How many minutes does Gina sing?

_____

4. Tom has 5 shelves in his book case. Each shelf has 21 chapter books and 31 picture books. How many books are on Tom's shelves in all?

_____

5. There are 11 students in the art club, 10 students in the math club, and 12 students in the computer club. There are twice as many students in band as in the art club, math club, and computer clubs put together. Write an equation to find how many students are in band.

_____

_____

6. Paula saw 6 yellow birds and x blue birds while bird watching. James saw twice as many birds as Paula did. James saw 26 birds. Write an equation to find how many blue birds Paula saw while bird watching.

_____

_____

Properties of Addition

CA Standards
KEY AF 1.2, MR 1.1

Addition Properties		
Commutative Property	$a + b = b + a$	$7 + 8 = 8 + 7$
Associative Property	$a + (b + c) = (a + b) + c$	$11 + (6 + 8) = (11 + 6) + 8$
Identity Property	$a + 0 = a$	$9 + 0 = 9$
	$0 + a = a$	$0 + 9 = 9$

Evaluate. Identify the property or properties you used.

1. $98 + 0$

_____

_____

2. $44 + 23 + 17$

_____

_____

3. $78 + 23 + b$, given $b = 12$

_____

_____

4. $71 + (45 + h)$, given $h = 9$

_____

_____

Use >, <, or = to make each statement true.

5. $59 + r$ ◯ $50 + 9 + r$

6. $(39 + 5) + 16$ ◯ $39 + (16 + 5)$

7. $41 + s + 45$ ◯ $41 + 54 + s$

8. $42 + j + 28$ ◯ $28 + j$

Spiral Review (Chapter 3, Lesson 3) **NS 1.0**

Write the value of the underlined digit.

9. 488.89<u>3</u>

10. 5<u>6</u>.901

11. 790.3<u>4</u>98

12. 5<u>6</u>,008,009

_____   _____   _____   _____

Properties of Addition

CA Standards
KEY AF 1.2, MR 1.1

Use properties to solve problems 1-6.

1. Julie and her friends bought tickets for rides at the fair. Julie bought 24 tickets. Dottie bought 29 tickets, and Carlos bought 36 tickets. How many tickets did they buy in all?

$$24 + 29 + 36 = 24 + \text{_____} + 29$$

$$= \text{_____} + 29$$

$$= \text{_____ tickets}$$

2. Stephen is preparing for his school's ice cream social. Stephen set 13 bowls on one table and 15 bowls on another table. He set 12 more bowls on a third table than on the first two combined. How many bowls did Stephen set on the third table?

$$(13 + 15) + 12 = \text{_____} + \text{_____} + $$

$$\text{_____}$$

$$= \text{_____} + \text{_____}$$

$$= \text{_____ bowls}$$

3. Craig and his brothers were playing a game. Craig's score was 41 points. Jake's score was 23 points. Noah's score was 19 points more than his brothers' scores combined. How many points did Noah score?

_____

4. Tom's class donates 47 cans of food to the local food pantry. Maria's class donates 32 cans of food. Jack's class donates 53 cans of food. How many cans of food were donated by the classes in all?

_____

5. Ginny played a game five times. She earned 57, 38, 75, 62, and 43 points. How many points did Ginny earn in all?

_____

6. Barry raked leaves Monday through Wednesday. He earned $12.25 on Monday and $7.45 on Tuesday. For the week, he earned $34.05. How much money did Barry earn on Wednesday?

_____

Properties of Multiplication

CA Standard
KEY AF 1.2

Properties of Multiplication		
Commutative Property	$a \times b = b \times a$	$6 \times 7 = 7 \times 6$
Associative Property	$a \times (b \times c) = (a \times b) \times c$	$2 \times (3 \times 5) = (2 \times 3) \times 5$
Identity Property	$a \times 1 = a$	$8 \times 1 = 8$
Zero Property	$a \times 0 = 0$	$4 \times 0 = 0$

Use properties to complete. Identify each property.

1. $5 \times (20 \times 12) = \square \times 12$ **2.** $35 \times 6 \times 0 = \square$ **3.** $25 \times 7 \times 4 = 25 \times \square \times 7$

_____   _____   _____

_____   _____   _____

Evaluate each expression, given $a = 6$, $b = 3$, and $c = 5$.

4. $a \times (b \times c)$ _____   **5.** $(a \times b) \times (c \times 0)$ _____

Compare. Write >, <, or = for each.

6. $(68 \times 2) \times 16$ $\bigcirc$ 68×16 **7.** $56 \times (8 \times 99)$ $\bigcirc$ $(56 \times 99) \times 8$

Spiral Review   (Chapter 5, Lesson 3) **KEY AF 1.2**

Evaluate each expression for $y = 4$.

8. $(16 \div y) + 15$ **9.** $4 + (y + 10)$ **10.** $(5 \times 4) - (y \times 4)$ **11.** $(20 - y) + (3 \times 4)$

_____   _____   _____   _____

Use with text pp. 128–131

Properties of Multiplication

CA Standard
KEY AF 1.2

Use rectangles and the Distributive Property to solve problems 1-6.

1. Rob had 5 coins in his coin collection before he went to two coin shows. After the first coin show, Rob had 7 times the amount of coins he had before the show. After the second coin show, Rob had 2 times the number of coins he had after the first show. How many coins did Rob have after the second coin show?

$$5 \times 7 \times 2 = 5 \times \text{\_\_\_\_\_} \times 7$$

$$= \text{\_\_\_\_\_} \times 7$$

$$= \text{\_\_\_\_\_} \text{ coins}$$

2. Mary has 25 blue beads. She has 3 times as many red beads as blue beads. She has 4 times as many yellow beads as red beads. How many yellow beads does Mary have?

$$(3 \times 25) \times 4 = \text{\_\_\_\_\_} \times (\text{\_\_\_\_\_} \times$$

$$\text{\_\_\_\_\_})$$

$$= \text{\_\_\_\_\_} \times \text{\_\_\_\_\_}$$

$$= \text{\_\_\_\_\_} \text{ yellow beads}$$

3. The third grade planted 4 trees on Arbor Day. The fourth grade planted 7 times the number of trees as the third grade planted. The fifth grade planted 5 times the number of trees as the fourth grade. How many trees did the fifth grade plant?

_____

4. Cans of pineapple juice come in packs of 6 cans. Packs of pineapple juice are placed in cartons with 4 packs in each carton. Cartons are placed in boxes with 50 cartons in each box. How many cans of pineapple juice are in 1 box?

_____

5. Maria had saved $4.00. Her mother gave her 2 times that amount to buy gifts for her sisters. In order to triple the total amount of money she had, Maria shoveled snow and did other chores. How much money does Maria have in all?

_____

6. Benny made bundles of 5 candles. He put the bundles in bags with 7 bundles in each bag. He placed the bags in crates with 6 bags in each crate. Then he packed boxes with 8 crates in each box. How many candles were in each box?

_____

Use with text pp. 128–131

Name _____ Date _____

Hands On: Add and Subtract Fractions with Like Denominators

CA Standards
KEY NS 2.3, MR 3.2

Add $\frac{1}{6} + \frac{1}{6}$.

Step 1

Add $\frac{1}{6} + \frac{1}{6}$

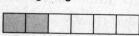

Solution: $\frac{1}{6} + \frac{1}{6} = \frac{1}{3}$

Step 2

Solve $\frac{1}{6} + \frac{1}{6} = \frac{2}{6}$

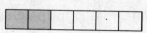

Step 3

Simplify $\frac{2}{6} = \frac{1}{3}$

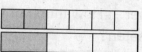

Subtract $\frac{3}{4} - \frac{1}{4}$.

Step 1

Subtract $\frac{3}{4} - \frac{1}{4}$

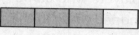

Solution: $\frac{3}{4} - \frac{1}{4} = \frac{1}{2}$

Step 2

Solve $\frac{3}{4} - \frac{1}{4} = \frac{2}{4}$

Step 3

Simplify $\frac{2}{4} = \frac{1}{2}$

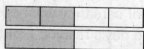

Find each sum or difference. Write each answer in simplest form.

1. $\frac{3}{8} - \frac{1}{8}$ _____

2. $\frac{7}{10} - \frac{1}{10}$ _____

3. $\frac{1}{4} + \frac{2}{4}$ _____

4. $\frac{4}{12} + \frac{2}{12}$ _____

5. $\frac{4}{5} - \frac{1}{5}$ _____

6. $\frac{3}{8} + \frac{1}{8}$ _____

7. $\frac{3}{10} + \frac{5}{10}$ _____

8. $\frac{5}{6} - \frac{3}{6}$ _____

Spiral Review (Chapter 5, Lesson 3) **KEY AF 1.2**

Evaluate each expression when $t = 5$.

9. $14 + t$ _____

10. $t - 1$ _____

11. Linda has a collection of dolls (t). She adds 2 more dolls to the collection. How many dolls does Linda now have? _____

Name _____ Date _____

Hands On: Add and Subtract Fractions with Like Denominators

Solve problems 1–6.

1. Jamal's mom bought a gallon of ice cream on Monday. That night the family ate $\frac{2}{6}$ of it. The next day, someone ate another $\frac{1}{6}$. How much of the ice cream was eaten?

_____

2. Kendra had $\frac{6}{8}$ of a box of popsicles to share with friends after school. They ate $\frac{4}{8}$ of the box. How much of a box of popsicles do they have now?

_____

3. The baseball team washed cars to raise money for new uniforms. They tallied the kinds of cars they washed. Here are the day's results: $\frac{3}{8}$ of the cars were compact, $\frac{4}{8}$ were SUV's and $\frac{1}{8}$ mini-vans. How many more of the cars were compact than mini-vans?

_____

4. Softball try-outs were held on Saturday. $\frac{3}{10}$ of the players who came wanted to pitch, $\frac{5}{10}$ hoped to be in the infield or outfield, and $\frac{2}{10}$ looked forward to being the catcher. What fraction of the players wanted to be the pitcher or catcher?

_____

5. A school is working hard to get a recycling program going. The surrounding community is helping by combining their recycling with the school's recycling. One day, there was $\frac{1}{12}$ flattened boxes, $\frac{2}{12}$ newspaper, $\frac{4}{12}$ used copy paper, $\frac{2}{12}$ cans and $\frac{1}{12}$ bottles. How much of the recycling was paper products?

_____

6. The Environmental Club at a school has decided to plant bulbs, bushes and trees in the spring. Each hallway has a flatbed for donated plants or bulbs. Hallway A has $\frac{1}{10}$ bulbs, $\frac{2}{10}$ small bushes and $\frac{7}{10}$ tree seedlings. Hallway B has $\frac{2}{10}$ bulbs, $\frac{1}{10}$ small bushes and $\frac{7}{10}$ tree seedlings. How many flatbeds of tree seedlings are there?

_____

Add and Subtract Fractions with Like Denominators

CA Standards
KEY NS 2.3, MR 1.1

Add $\frac{7}{14} + \frac{3}{14}$.

Step ①	Step ②
Add $\frac{7}{14} + \frac{3}{14} = \frac{10}{14}$	Simplify $\frac{7}{14} + \frac{3}{14} = \frac{10}{14} = \frac{5}{7}$
Solution: $\frac{7}{14} + \frac{3}{14} = \frac{5}{7}$	

Subtract $\frac{11}{12} - \frac{5}{12}$.

Step ①	Step ②
Subtract $\frac{11}{12} - \frac{5}{12} = \frac{6}{12}$	Simplify $\frac{11}{12} - \frac{5}{12} = \frac{6}{12} = \frac{1}{2}$
Solution: $\frac{11}{12} - \frac{5}{12} = \frac{1}{2}$	

Add or subtract. Write each answer in simplest form.

1. $\frac{3}{8} + \frac{3}{8}$ _____

2. $\frac{9}{10} - \frac{3}{10}$ _____

3. $\frac{3}{8} + \frac{1}{8}$ _____

4. $\frac{8}{15} - \frac{3}{15}$ _____

5. $\frac{5}{6} + \frac{1}{6}$ _____

6. $\frac{7}{8} - \frac{5}{8}$ _____

7. $\frac{4}{7} - \frac{2}{7}$ _____

8. $\frac{9}{16} + \frac{1}{16}$ _____

Spiral Review (Chapter 5, Lesson 3) **KEY** AF 1.2, AF 1.0

Evaluate each expression when $n = 6$.

9. $12 - n$ _____

10. $n + 9$ _____

11. Juan had a bag of 12 candies. He lost some of them while riding home on his bike. Write the expression for the number of candies he has now. _____

Name _____ Date _____

Add and Subtract Fractions with Like Denominators

Solve. Write each answer in simplest form.

1. Megan filled $\frac{3}{9}$ of a fruit basket with red delicious apples and $\frac{3}{9}$ with Bartlett pears. How much of the basket is apples and pears?

_____

2. Machito had $\frac{5}{8}$ of a box of oranges and ate $\frac{1}{8}$ of the box. What part of the box of oranges is left?

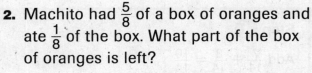

_____

3. $\frac{9}{16}$ of the United States' citrus crop grows in the state of Florida and $\frac{5}{16}$ in California. How much more of the country's citrus fruits comes from Florida?

_____

4. $\frac{5}{12}$ of Florida's citrus crop is oranges. $\frac{3}{12}$ of the citrus crop is grapefruit. How much of the state's citrus crop is oranges and grapefruit?

_____

5. If Florida's citrus crop is $\frac{5}{12}$ oranges, $\frac{3}{12}$ grapefruit, $\frac{2}{12}$ lemons and the rest tangerines, how much of the crop is tangerines?

_____

6. Suppose two trucks containing $\frac{5}{6}$ each of California navel oranges, come in to a distribution center. How many truckloads of California navel oranges are waiting to go out to grocery stores?

_____

Name _____ Date _____

Hands On: Add and Subtract Fractions with Unlike Denominators

CA Standards
KEY NS 2.3, MR 3.2

Add $\frac{1}{3} + \frac{1}{6}$.

Step 1

Add $\frac{1}{3} + \frac{1}{6}$

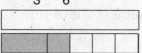

Solution: $\frac{1}{3} + \frac{1}{6} = \frac{3}{6}$

Step 2

Make a row of tiles the same length, but use like tiles. $\frac{1}{3} + \frac{1}{6} = \frac{1}{6} + \frac{1}{6} + \frac{1}{6} = \frac{3}{6}$

Subtract $\frac{3}{4} - \frac{1}{3}$.

Step 1

Subtract $\frac{3}{4} - \frac{1}{3}$

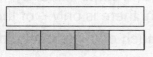

Solution: $\frac{3}{4} - \frac{1}{3} = \frac{5}{12}$

Step 2

Find fraction tiles with like units that fit in the space and show the difference between $\frac{3}{4}$ and $\frac{1}{3}$. Do $\frac{1}{12}$ tiles work?

$\frac{3}{4} - \frac{1}{3} = \frac{9}{12} - \frac{4}{12} = \frac{5}{12}$

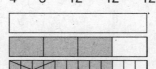

Find each sum or difference.

1. $\frac{3}{12} - \frac{1}{6}$ _____

2. $\frac{3}{5} - \frac{2}{10}$ _____

3. $\frac{1}{4} + \frac{2}{8}$ _____

4. $\frac{2}{6} + \frac{6}{12}$ _____

Spiral Review (Chapter 4, Lesson 1) **KEY** NS 1.5

Write each fraction or mixed number in decimal form.

5. $1\frac{1}{5}$ _____

6. $3\frac{3}{4}$ _____

7. Brandon is working hard to increase his speed while running a mile. He hopes to be able to run that distance in $4\frac{1}{4}$ minutes by next year. He jots this goal into his practice log as a decimal. What did he write? _____

Hands On: Add and Subtract Fractions with Unlike Denominators

Solve problems 1–6.

1. The Jones family is leaving on vacation. They fill $\frac{2}{5}$ of their van's cargo space with the children's luggage and $\frac{3}{10}$ with their parents' suitcases. How much of the cargo space is filled?

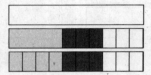

_____

2. The family rearranges their bags so that $\frac{1}{3}$ of the space is free. Then they use $\frac{1}{12}$ of the space for a forgotten bag. How much free space is there now?

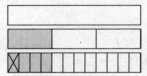

_____

3. The Jones family will be traveling cross country. During the early morning rush, they travel $\frac{1}{10}$ of the distance planned for the day. By lunch time they have gone another $\frac{2}{5}$ of the way. How far has the family traveled?

_____

4. The family stops for lunch and gets a $\frac{1}{2}$ bucket of chicken and some salad. By the time they finish, there is only $\frac{1}{8}$ of the bucket left. How much of the bucket did they eat?

_____

5. The family reaches a state park and stops to hike. The Red Trail is $\frac{1}{2}$ mile long. The Blue Trail is $\frac{2}{3}$ of a mile. The Yellow Trail is $\frac{5}{12}$ of a mile. What is the total distance of the park's three trails?

_____

6. They read about a new trail which is being constructed. It will be the park's longest at $1\frac{1}{2}$ miles. How much longer than the Blue Trail will it be?

_____

Add and Subtract Fractions with Unlike Denominators

CA Standard
KEY NS 2.3

Add $\frac{1}{3} + \frac{1}{4}$.

Step 1

Find a common denominator. Since 4 is not a multiple of 3, multiply 3×4. 12 is the common denominator.

Solution: $\frac{1}{3} + \frac{1}{4} = \frac{7}{12}$

Step 2

Rewrite the problem.
Then add. Write the answer in simplest form.

$\frac{1}{3} = \frac{4}{12}$

$\frac{1}{4} = \frac{3}{12}$

$\frac{4}{12} + \frac{3}{12} = \frac{7}{12}$

Subtract $\frac{2}{3} - \frac{1}{6}$.

Step 1

Find a common denominator. Since 6 is a multiple of 3, you can use 6 as the common denominator.

Solution: $\frac{2}{3} - \frac{1}{6} = \frac{1}{2}$

Step 2

Rewrite the problem.

Then subtract. Write the answer in simplest form.

$\frac{2}{3} = \frac{4}{6}$

$\frac{4}{6} - \frac{1}{6} = \frac{3}{6} = \frac{1}{2}$

Add or subtract. Write each answer in simplest form.

1. $\frac{3}{4} - \frac{1}{3}$ _____

2. $\frac{7}{10} - \frac{1}{4}$ _____

3. $\frac{1}{3} + \frac{2}{4}$ _____

4. $\frac{4}{10} + \frac{1}{3}$ _____

5. $\frac{2}{3} - \frac{1}{5}$ _____

6. $\frac{3}{5} + \frac{1}{3}$ _____

7. $\frac{3}{10} + \frac{9}{20}$ _____

8. $\frac{5}{8} - \frac{1}{4}$ _____

Spiral Review (Chapter 4, Lesson 1) **KEY** NS 1.5, MR 2.3

Write each fraction in decimal form.

9. $\frac{3}{4}$ _____

10. $\frac{1}{5}$ _____

11. A soccer team was able to complete $\frac{7}{10}$ of their drills during a two-hour practice session. They must fill out a log sheet reporting the portion of exercises not finished in decimal form.

_____

Add and Subtract Fractions with Unlike Denominators

CA Standard
KEY NS 2.3

Solve problems 1–6.

1. Sameena filled $\frac{3}{8}$ of a pizza with mushrooms and $\frac{1}{2}$ with onions. How much of the pizza is covered with vegetables?

_____

2. Dondre' bought $\frac{3}{4}$ of a pound of ground beef for cheeseburger pizza. He used $\frac{2}{3}$ of a pound to make it. How much meat is left?

_____

3. Kady made a pizza that was $\frac{3}{10}$ pineapple and $\frac{1}{2}$ ham. The rest was plain. How much of Kady's pizza is plain?

_____

4. Yon Sue made her pizza with $\frac{5}{8}$ cup chopped broccoli and $\frac{3}{16}$ cup green pepper. How much more of the pizza has broccoli on it than green pepper?

_____

5. A pizza shop bought a bushel of fresh vegetables. $\frac{4}{15}$ of the bushel was used on Friday, $\frac{3}{5}$ on Saturday and $\frac{2}{15}$ on Sunday. How much of the bushel is left for Monday?

_____

6. A pizza shop took a poll of favorite toppings over a month's time. $\frac{1}{4}$ of the customers' votes were for pepperoni, $\frac{7}{16}$ for sausage, $\frac{3}{16}$ for peppers and $\frac{1}{8}$ for mushrooms. How many more of the customers' votes were for meat than for vegetables?

_____

Name _____ . Date _____

Problem Solving: Work Backward

CA Standards
MR 2.6, KEY NS 2.3

Use the Word Backward strategy to solve. Explain why your answer makes sense.

Chloe had a certain amount of fruit juice set aside for a party. She had $\frac{1}{5}$ gallon less orange juice than the entire amount of fruit juice. She had $\frac{3}{4}$ gallon less apple juice than orange juice. She had $\frac{1}{4}$ gallon more grape juice than apple juice. If she had $\frac{2}{5}$ gallon grape juice, how much fruit juice did she have?

Grape Juice		Apple Juice		Orange Juice		Fruit Juice
$\frac{2}{5}$ gallon	$-\frac{1}{4}$	$\frac{3}{20}$ gallon	$+\frac{3}{4}$	$\frac{18}{20}$ gallon	$+\frac{1}{5}$	$\frac{22}{20}$
This is $\frac{1}{4}$ gallon more than apple juice.	Work backward. Subtract $\frac{1}{4}$. $\frac{2}{5} - \frac{1}{4}$ $= \frac{8}{20} - \frac{5}{20}$ $= \frac{3}{20}$	This is $\frac{3}{4}$ gallon less than orange juice.	Work backward. Add $\frac{3}{4}$. $\frac{3}{20} + \frac{3}{4}$ $= \frac{3}{20} + \frac{15}{20}$ $= \frac{18}{20}$	This is $\frac{1}{5}$ gallon less than the total amount of fruit juice.	Work backward. Add $\frac{1}{5}$ $\frac{18}{20} + \frac{1}{5}$ $= \frac{18}{20} + \frac{4}{20}$ $= \frac{22}{20}$	

Solution: Chloe had $\frac{22}{20}$ gallon or $1\frac{1}{10}$ gallon of fruit juice.

1. Calvin spent a certain amount of time doing chores around the house. He spent $\frac{1}{2}$ hour more cleaning his room than washing the dishes. He spent $\frac{1}{4}$ hour more washing the dishes than taking out the trash. He spent $\frac{1}{6}$ hour taking out the trash. How much time did Calvin spend cleaning his room?

_____

Spiral Review (Chapter 4, Lesson 2) **MR 2.3**

Write each fraction or mixed number as a decimal.

2. $2\frac{3}{4}$ _____

3. $\frac{3}{5}$ _____

4. Jonas drank $\frac{7}{8}$ of a glass of milk. What is $\frac{7}{8}$ written as a decimal? Round to the nearest hundredth.

_____

Problem Solving: Work Backward

Use the Work Backward strategy to solve. Explain why your answer makes sense.

1. Anna and Kirby went running together on Saturday and Sunday. Kirby ran $\frac{1}{3}$ mile more than Anna on Saturday. Kirby ran a total of 3 miles on Saturday. How many miles did Anna run?

   $3 - \frac{1}{3} =$ _____

2. Angela made a side salad for dinner. She put in $\frac{3}{4}$ cup more lettuce than tomato in the salad. She put $\frac{1}{4}$ cup more cucumber than tomato in the salad. She put $\frac{1}{2}$ cup cucumber in the salad. How much lettuce did Angela put in her salad?

   $\frac{1}{2} - \frac{1}{4} =$ _____

   _____ $+ \frac{3}{4} =$ _____

3. Greg's family went on vacation and kept track of the amount of gasoline they used over the 3 days. On the second day, they used $\frac{3}{5}$ of a tank more than on the first day. On the third day, they used $\frac{1}{3}$ of a tank less than on the second day. They used $\frac{4}{5}$ of a tank on the third day. How much gas did they use on the first day?

   _____

4. Tim bought a certain amount of green paint for a picture he was painting. He bought $\frac{3}{4}$ pint more yellow than green paint. He bought $\frac{5}{8}$ pint less blue paint than yellow paint. If he bought $\frac{1}{4}$ pint of blue paint, how much green paint did Tim buy?

   _____

5. Mariah's class collected soup labels to raise money for their school. Each day they placed the collected labels in a jar to see how much they collected that day. They kept track of how much they collected over a week. On Tuesday, they collected $\frac{1}{8}$ jar more than on Monday. On Wednesday, they collected $\frac{1}{2}$ jar more than on Tuesday. On Thursday, they collected $\frac{1}{4}$ jar less than on Wednesday. On Friday, they collected $\frac{3}{8}$ more than on Thursday. On Friday, $\frac{3}{4}$ of the jar was filled with soup labels. How much of a jar did they collect on Monday?

   _____

6. Susan knit a blanket for her niece. Susan put $\frac{1}{3}$ more pink yarn than purple yarn in the blanket. There is $\frac{5}{9}$ less purple yarn than white yarn. The blanket is $\frac{3}{4}$ white yarn. How much of the blanket is pink yarn?

   _____

Hands On: Sums Greater Than 1

CA Standards
KEY NS 2.3, MR 2.3

Use Fraction Tiles to Add $\frac{2}{3} + \frac{3}{4}$.

Step 1 Place two $\frac{1}{3}$ tiles and three $\frac{1}{4}$ tiles under one whole bar.

$\frac{1}{3}$	$\frac{1}{3}$

$\frac{1}{4}$	$\frac{1}{4}$	$\frac{1}{4}$

1

Step 2 Find like fraction tiles that make a row the same length as the sum of $\frac{2}{3}$ and $\frac{3}{4}$.

Step 3 Add, writing the sum as a mixed number in simplest form:

$$\frac{2}{3} + \frac{3}{4} = \frac{17}{12} = 1\frac{5}{12}$$

Write the equation illustrated by the model. Write the sum as a mixed number in simplest form.

1.

1

$\frac{1}{5}$	$\frac{1}{5}$	$\frac{1}{5}$

$\frac{1}{10}$	$\frac{1}{10}$	$\frac{1}{10}$	$\frac{1}{10}$	$\frac{1}{10}$	$\frac{1}{10}$

$\frac{1}{5}$	$\frac{1}{5}$	$\frac{1}{5}$	$\frac{1}{5}$	$\frac{1}{5}$	$\frac{1}{5}$

_____

2.

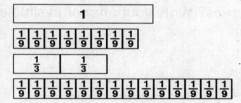

_____

Add. Write each sum as a mixed number in simplest form.

3. $\frac{2}{3} + \frac{5}{6}$ _____   **4.** $\frac{1}{4} + \frac{7}{8}$ _____   **5.** $\frac{3}{4} + \frac{1}{2}$ _____   **6.** $\frac{3}{4} + \frac{2}{5}$ _____

Spiral Review (Chapter 5, Lesson 5) **KEY** AF 1.5, AF 1.0

7. Complete the function table to find the value of *y*.

Week *x*	1	2	3	4	5	6	7
Allowance saved (dollars) *y*	$4	$8	$12				

8. Write an equation for the function table. _____

Homework

71

Use with text pp. 168–169

Hands On: Sums Greater Than 1

CA Standards
KEY NS 2.3, MR 2.3

Solve Problems 1–6.

1. Sally and Tyrell each have $\frac{2}{3}$ of a cup of lemonade. How much do they have all together? Write your answer as a mixed number.

1

$\frac{1}{3}$	$\frac{1}{3}$	$\frac{1}{3}$	$\frac{1}{3}$

_____

2. Jackson and Chase are having lunch. Jackson eats $\frac{7}{16}$ of a pizza, and Chase eats $\frac{5}{8}$ of a pizza. How much pizza have Jackson and Chase eaten?

3. Jerice has $\frac{2}{3}$ of a pound of cherries. Andy has $\frac{5}{6}$ of a pound of cherries. How much will they have if they combine their cherries? Write your answer in simplest form.

_____

4. Kevin walks $\frac{7}{8}$ of a mile from Elm Street to Oak Street. Maple Street is $\frac{3}{4}$ of a mile south of Oak Street. If he continues to Maple Street, how far will Kevin have walked?

_____

5. Chad is making salsa for a party. The recipe calls for $\frac{5}{6}$ of a cup of tomatoes, $\frac{3}{4}$ of a cup of onions, and $\frac{1}{2}$ of a cup of cilantro. What is the total amount of ingredients needed to make salsa? Write a number sentence to show your answer.

_____

6. Mark's recipe for burritos calls for $\frac{2}{3}$ cup of Monterey Jack cheese and $\frac{1}{4}$ cup of Cheddar cheese. The recipe makes 4 burritos. Mark is expecting 8 people for dinner. Half of them will each eat one burrito, and the others will each eat two. What is the total amount of cheese that Mark will need? Write your answer in simplest terms.

_____

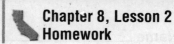

Add a Fraction and a Mixed Number

Add $1\frac{1}{2} + \frac{3}{5}$.

Step 1 Find a common denominator for the fractions. Multiply the denominators.

$2 \times 5 = 10$

Step 2 Rewrite the fractions using the common denominator.

$\frac{1}{2} = \frac{5}{10}$

$\frac{3}{5} = \frac{6}{10}$

Step 3 Add the fractions.

$\frac{5}{10} + \frac{6}{10} = \frac{11}{10}$.

There is only one whole number: 1

$1 + \frac{11}{10} = 1\frac{11}{10}$

Solution: $1\frac{1}{2} + \frac{3}{5} = 2\frac{1}{10}$

Step 4 Simplify the sum if possible.

$1\frac{11}{10} = 2\frac{1}{10}$

Add. Write each sum in the simplest form.

1. $8\frac{1}{2} + \frac{2}{3} =$ _____

2. $2\frac{3}{7} + \frac{6}{7} =$ _____

3. $8\frac{1}{6} + \frac{1}{2} =$ _____

4. $\frac{5}{7} + 4\frac{1}{2} =$ _____

Spiral Review (Chapter 5, Lesson 5) **KEY** AF 1.5, AF 1.0

5. Complete the function table to find the value of y.

Day x	1	2	3	4	5	6	7
Amount collected (pennies) y	15	30	45				

6. Write an equation for the function table. _____

Name _____   Date _____

Add a Fraction and a Mixed Number

Solve Problems 1–6.

1. Andrea is measuring water for a science experiment. She already has $1\frac{1}{3}$ cups of water in her measuring beaker, and then adds another $\frac{2}{3}$ cup of water. How much water does she have in all?

_____

2. Halley is also measuring water. She has $1\frac{1}{2}$ cups and adds $\frac{1}{3}$ cup. How much water does she have in all? Hint: multiply 2×3 to find a common denominator, then add.

_____

3. Beth is making a pie and has $2\frac{1}{3}$ cup of sugar. She realizes she needs $\frac{1}{6}$ cup more for the recipe. How much sugar does the recipe need in all?

_____

4. James is building a dollhouse for his little brother and sister. He has pieces of carpet $5\frac{3}{5}$ inches long and $4\frac{1}{3}$ inches long. Put end to end, are these two pieces long enough to cover a floor that is 10 inches long? Explain your answer.

_____

_____

5. Evelyn and Ferris are on the stage crew for the school play. They need to put tape on the stage to mark where the performers should stand. The director gave them this list. How much tape do they need in all?

$1\frac{3}{4}$ feet : 2 pieces
$\frac{2}{3}$ foot : 6 pieces
$\frac{5}{6}$ foot : 4 pieces

_____

6. Peter and Susan are making costumes for the school play. They went to the store to buy fabric for the animals' costumes. The two bears each need $4\frac{1}{4}$ yards of brown fabric. The rabbit needs $3\frac{2}{3}$ yards of brown fabric, and the squirrel needs $2\frac{3}{8}$ yards of brown fabric. How much brown fabric do Peter and Susan need?

_____

Add Mixed Numbers with and without Regrouping

CA Standards
KEY NS 2.3, MR 2.4

Add $2\frac{5}{6} + 3\frac{2}{3}$.

Step ① Use a common denominator to find equivalent fractions.	Step ② Add the fractions.	Step ③ Add the whole numbers. Simplify.
$2\frac{5}{6} = 2\frac{10}{12}$ $3\frac{2}{3} = 3\frac{8}{12}$	$\begin{array}{r} 2\frac{10}{12} \\ + 3\frac{8}{12} \\ \hline \frac{18}{12} \end{array}$	$\begin{array}{r} 2\frac{10}{12} \\ + 3\frac{8}{12} \\ \hline \end{array}$ $5\frac{18}{12} = 6\frac{6}{12} = 6\frac{1}{2}$

Add. Write each sum in simplest form.

1. $3\frac{2}{3} + 1\frac{1}{4}$

2. $4\frac{1}{2} + 2\frac{3}{8}$

3. $7\frac{1}{3} + 3\frac{1}{2}$

4. $1\frac{4}{5} + 2\frac{1}{2}$

5. $6\frac{3}{5} + 4\frac{7}{10}$

6. $5\frac{2}{3} + 1\frac{3}{4}$

7. $\begin{array}{r} 9\frac{1}{2} \\ + 4\frac{2}{3} \\ \hline \end{array}$

8. $\begin{array}{r} 5\frac{3}{8} \\ + 1\frac{3}{4} \\ \hline \end{array}$

9. $\begin{array}{r} 1\frac{9}{10} \\ + 7\frac{4}{5} \\ \hline \end{array}$

Evaluate the expression. Write your answer in simplest form.

10. Evaluate $1\frac{1}{3} + y$, if $y = 3\frac{5}{8}$.

11. Evaluate $3\frac{2}{5} + y$, if $y = 2\frac{1}{10}$.

Spiral Review (Chapter 7, Lesson 1) **KEY NS 2.3, MR 3.2**

Solve.

12. $5 + \frac{1}{2}$

13. $\frac{3}{5} + 4$

14. Juanita has $\frac{2}{3}$ of a candy bar. Max gives her a whole candy bar. How many candy bars does Juanita have now?

Name _____ Date _____

Add Mixed Numbers with and without Regrouping

Solve Problems 1–6.

1. Paulina used $4\frac{1}{2}$ yards of red cloth and $2\frac{1}{4}$ yards of blue cloth to make a costume. How much cloth did she use altogether? Hint: use 4 as the common denominator.

$$\frac{1}{2} = \frac{2}{4}$$

_____

2. Denise baked $2\frac{1}{2}$ trays of sugar cookies and $1\frac{3}{4}$ trays of peanut butter cookies. How many trays of cookies did she bake in all? Express your answer in simplest form.

_____

3. Denise also baked $2\frac{3}{5}$ trays of chocolate chip cookies and $1\frac{2}{7}$ trays of oatmeal raisin cookies. How many trays of chocolate chip and oatmeal raisin cookies did she bake in all?

_____

4. Felicia spent $3\frac{3}{4}$ hours completing her science project on Monday, and then $2\frac{2}{6}$ hours on Tuesday. How many hours in all did Felicia spend on her science project?

_____

5. Andrew and Becky do chores on the weekend to earn their allowance. Last weekend they each spent $2\frac{1}{2}$ hours doing laundry, $1\frac{5}{20}$ hours cleaning the house, and $1\frac{3}{4}$ hours raking leaves. How many hours did they each spend on chores last weekend? Write your answer in simplest form.

_____

6. Andrew and Becky each earn $3 an hour for doing chores. They are going to combine their allowances to buy a video game. How much money do Andrew and Becky have to spend on a video game?

_____

Name _____ Date _____

Hands On: Rename to Subtract

CA Standards
KEY NS 2.3, NS 2.0

Use Fraction Tiles to model $2 - 1\frac{3}{5}$.

Step 1 Use two whole fraction tiles to represent 2.	**Step 2** Rename one whole tile as $\frac{5}{5}$ using five $\frac{1}{5}$ tiles.	**Step 3** Subtract $1\frac{3}{5}$ by taking away one whole tile and 3 of the $\frac{1}{5}$ tiles. The remaining tiles show the difference.
[1] [1]	[1] [$\frac{1}{5}$ $\frac{1}{5}$ $\frac{1}{5}$ $\frac{1}{5}$ $\frac{1}{5}$]	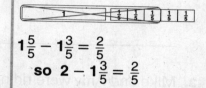 $1\frac{5}{5} - 1\frac{3}{5} = \frac{2}{5}$ so $2 - 1\frac{3}{5} = \frac{2}{5}$

Use fraction tiles to rename the whole number. Subtract the mixed number from the whole number. Sketch your model.

1. $3 - 1\frac{2}{3}$ _____

2. $3 - 1\frac{5}{6}$ _____

3. $4 - 2\frac{5}{9}$ _____

4. $3 - 1\frac{3}{8}$ _____

5. $4 - 1\frac{5}{7}$ _____

6. $2 - 1\frac{2}{5}$ _____

7. $2 - 1\frac{1}{6}$ _____

8. $3 - 2\frac{3}{10}$ _____

9. $4 - 2\frac{1}{5}$ _____

10. Sketch three different ways to show the number 6 as a mixed number.

Spiral Review (Chapter 4, Lesson 2) **KEY NS 1.2**

Write the decimal as a fraction or a mixed number.

11. 0.25 _____

12. 1.75 _____

13. 0.8 _____

14. 2.65 _____

15. 5.9 _____

Write the fraction as a decimal.

16. $\frac{1}{10}$ _____

17. $\frac{25}{100}$ _____

18. $\frac{2}{5}$ _____

19. $\frac{27}{100}$ _____

20. $\frac{6}{100}$ _____

Name _____ Date _____

Hands On: Rename to Subtract

CA Standards
KEY NS 2.3, NS 2.0

Use fraction tiles to rename the whole number for problems 1–6.

1. Pauline is subtracting $4 - 1\frac{2}{3}$. She made this model to rename 4 as $3\frac{3}{3}$. What should she write for an answer?

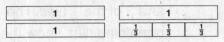

2. Sara has to subtract $2 - 1\frac{4}{5}$. How should she rename 2? What should she write for her answer?

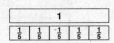

_____

3. Mike and Amy were riding their bikes on a camp trail. Amy rode 3 miles, and Mike rode $2\frac{5}{8}$ miles. How much farther did Amy ride than Mike?

_____

4. Carolyn was jogging on a trail. She ran $2\frac{5}{12}$ miles of the 4 mile trail. How much further would she have had to jog to complete the 4 mile trail?

_____

5. Erin brought 8 cookies to share with her friend Dianna, but gave the dog one cookie. Of the remaining cookies, Erin ate two cookies and Dianna ate $\frac{19}{7}$ cookies. How many cookies were left?

_____

6. Alyce and Julie were sitting by the pool eating lunch. Alyce took out six sandwiches cut into quarters, but dropped one whole sandwich and three quarters into the pool. If Alyce and Julie split the remaining sandwiches equally, how many sandwiches would each one get?

_____

Rename to Subtract

CA Standards
KEY NS 2.3, NS 2.0

Find $3 - 1\frac{3}{8}$.

Step ① Rename 3 as 2 + 1. Then rename 1 as a fraction, using 8 for the denominator. $3 = 2\frac{8}{8}$

Step ② Subtract the fractions. $\frac{8}{8} - \frac{3}{8} = \frac{5}{8}$

Step ③ Subtract the whole numbers. $2 - 1 = 1$

Step ④ Use addition to check your work. $1\frac{5}{8} + 1\frac{3}{8} = 2\frac{8}{8} = 3$

Subtract. Check your answers.

1. $\begin{array}{r} 9 \\ -\ 7\frac{1}{14} \\ \hline \end{array}$

2. $\begin{array}{r} 3 \\ -\ 1\frac{1}{3} \\ \hline \end{array}$

3. $\begin{array}{r} 7 \\ -\ 2\frac{5}{8} \\ \hline \end{array}$

4. $\begin{array}{r} 4 \\ -\ 1\frac{1}{4} \\ \hline \end{array}$

5. $\begin{array}{r} 15 \\ -\ 8\frac{5}{6} \\ \hline \end{array}$

6. $\begin{array}{r} 2 \\ -\ 1\frac{4}{5} \\ \hline \end{array}$

7. $\begin{array}{r} 6 \\ -\ 5\frac{7}{18} \\ \hline \end{array}$

8. $\begin{array}{r} 12 \\ -\ 9\frac{2}{3} \\ \hline \end{array}$

9. $\begin{array}{r} 5 \\ -\ 4\frac{3}{25} \\ \hline \end{array}$

10. $\begin{array}{r} 13 \\ -\ 6\frac{9}{14} \\ \hline \end{array}$

11. $24 - 6\frac{6}{13}$

12. $8 - 2\frac{1}{3}$

13. $6 - 1\frac{3}{7}$

14. $18 - 15\frac{6}{7}$

15. $9 - 6\frac{14}{15}$

16. $12 - 3\frac{4}{5}$

17. $36 - 14\frac{4}{9}$

18. $19 - 4\frac{7}{18}$

Spiral Review (Chapter 4, Lesson 2) **KEY NS 1.2**

Write the decimal as a fraction or a mixed number.

19. 2.75

20. 0.25

21. 0.37

22. 1.17

23. 0.7

Write the fraction as a decimal.

24. $\frac{3}{5}$

25. $\frac{7}{10}$

26. $\frac{49}{100}$

27. $\frac{3}{4}$

28. $\frac{1}{2}$

Name _____ Date _____

Rename to Subtract

CA Standards
KEY NS 2.3, NS 2.0

Solve problems 1–6.

1. Bobby bought a new door that was 31 inches wide. He can't fit a door wider than $29\frac{1}{2}$ inches into his door frame, so he needs to trim the new door. How much does he have to cut off the width of the new door to make it fit?

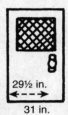

29½ in.
31 in.

_____

2. Bobby's new door is also too tall. It is 75 inches tall, but the door frame will only hold a door up to $73\frac{5}{8}$ inches. How much does he have to cut off the height of the door to make it fit?

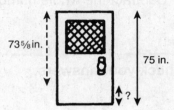

73⅝ in.   75 in.
?

_____

3. Anita must be 5 feet tall to ride the water slide at the park. She is $4\frac{1}{4}$ feet tall. How much taller does Anita need to be to ride the water slide?

_____

4. George read 4 books this week. Last week, George read $2\frac{5}{9}$ books. How many more books did George read this week than last week?

_____

5. Peter and Chu-nan read comic books for an hour. Chu-nan read two comic books, each 10 pages long. Peter read $8\frac{5}{6}$ pages each of two comic books. How many more pages did Chun-nan read than Peter?

_____

6. John, Chip, Alex, and Gretchen went to the county fair. By the end of the day, John and Gretchen had each eaten 2 cups of ice cream and split a third one. Chip and Alex ate $4\frac{3}{4}$ cups of ice cream together. Who ate more ice cream: John and Gretchen or Chip and Alex? How much more did they eat?

_____

_____

_____

Name _____ Date _____

Subtract Mixed Numbers with Like Denominators

CA Standards
KEY NS 2.3, NS 2.0

Find $3\frac{1}{5} - 1\frac{2}{5}$.

Step 1 Rename $3\frac{1}{5}$. $3\frac{1}{5} = 2 + 1 + \frac{1}{5} = 2 + \frac{5}{5} + \frac{1}{5} = 2\frac{6}{5}$

Step 2 Subtract the fractions. $\frac{6}{5} - \frac{2}{5} = \frac{4}{5}$

Step 3 Subtract the whole numbers. $2 - 1 = 1$

Step 4 Write the difference in simplest form. $3\frac{1}{5} - 1\frac{2}{5} = 1\frac{4}{5}$

Subtract. Write the difference in simplest form.

1. $5\frac{4}{7}$
   $- 3\frac{6}{7}$

2. $8\frac{1}{4}$
   $- 2\frac{3}{4}$

3. $11\frac{3}{9}$
   $- 4\frac{5}{9}$

4. $12\frac{7}{9}$
   $- 9\frac{8}{9}$

5. $3\frac{2}{6}$
   $- 2\frac{5}{6}$

6. $3\frac{4}{8}$
   $- 1\frac{7}{8}$

7. $4\frac{2}{5}$
   $- 2\frac{4}{5}$

8. $6\frac{1}{3}$
   $- 4\frac{2}{3}$

9. $5\frac{3}{7}$
   $- 4\frac{5}{7}$

10. $3\frac{9}{13}$
    $- 1\frac{11}{13}$

11. $2\frac{1}{4} - 1\frac{3}{4}$

12. $3\frac{3}{8} - 1\frac{6}{8}$

13. $16\frac{1}{12} - 7\frac{5}{12}$

14. $5\frac{2}{6} - 1\frac{5}{6}$

15. $5\frac{1}{3} - 3\frac{2}{3}$

16. $11\frac{3}{10} - 6\frac{7}{10}$

17. $7\frac{2}{7} - 4\frac{5}{7}$

18. $10\frac{2}{9} - 7\frac{7}{9}$

Spiral Review (Chapter 6, Lessons 3 and 4) **KEY AF 1.2**

Find the missing number. Identify the property you used.

19. $73 = 73 + \boxed{}$

20. $12 \times 9 = \boxed{} \times 12$

21. $(14 + 5) + 32 = 14 + (\boxed{} + 32)$

Use with text pp. 190–191

Name _____ Date _____

Subtract Mixed Numbers with Like Denominators

CA Standards
KEY NS 2.3, NS 2.0

Solve problems 1–6. Write your answer in simplest form.

1. Courtney and Don were working in their garden. Courtney planted $6\frac{1}{3}$ rows of peas. Don planted $4\frac{2}{3}$ rows of peas. How many more rows of peas did Courtney plant?

$$6\frac{1}{3} = 6 + \frac{1}{3}$$
$$= 5 + 1 + \frac{1}{3}$$
$$= 5\frac{4}{3}$$
$$= 5\frac{4}{3} - 4\frac{2}{3} =$$

_____

2. Before they were ready to plant, Don weeded $16\frac{3}{8}$ rows of the garden. Courtney weeded $13\frac{5}{8}$ rows. How much more did Don weed?

_____

3. Jill and Marsha were selling soft drinks at lunch to raise money for their class trip. Jill sold $4\frac{7}{8}$ gallons of root beer. Marsha sold $5\frac{3}{8}$ gallons of root beer. How much more root beer did Marsha sell?

_____

4. In addition to selling soft drinks, Jill and Marsha also decided to sell bags of popcorn. Jill sold $18\frac{1}{2}$ bags of popcorn, and Marsha sold $12\frac{1}{2}$ bags of popcorn. Who sold more popcorn, and by how much?

_____

5. Ben and Mary were climbing trees in their back yard. Mary climbed a tree $2\frac{3}{10}$ meters tall. Ben got halfway up a tree $4\frac{2}{5}$ meters tall. Who climbed higher? By how much?

_____

6. Kieran and Melissa were listening to the radio. Kieran chose a station and they listened to 12 songs. When the 13th song was $\frac{1}{3}$ of the way over, Melissa changed the station. They then listened to 9 songs on the new station. When the 10th song was $\frac{2}{3}$ of the way over, Kieran changed the station again. How many more songs did they listen to on Kieran's station than on Melissa's?

_____

Name _____ Date _____

Subtract Mixed Numbers

CA Standards
KEY NS 2.3, NS 2.0

Find $5\frac{1}{2} - 1\frac{7}{8}$.

Step 1 Use the LCD to find equivalent fractions.

$$5\frac{1}{2} = \quad 5\frac{4}{8}$$
$$-1\frac{7}{8} = \quad -1\frac{7}{8}$$

Step 2 Rename the mixed numbers.

$$5\frac{4}{8} = \quad 4\frac{12}{8}$$
$$-1\frac{7}{8} = \quad -1\frac{7}{8}$$

Step 3 Subtract and simplify.

$$4\frac{12}{8}$$
$$-1\frac{7}{8}$$
$$\overline{3\frac{5}{8}}$$

Subtract. Write each difference in simplest form.

1. $9\frac{1}{2}$
    $-3\frac{3}{8}$

2. $7\frac{1}{8}$
    $-2\frac{3}{6}$

3. $7\frac{1}{5}$
    $-2\frac{1}{8}$

4. $4\frac{1}{4}$
    $-2\frac{5}{6}$

5. $9\frac{1}{8}$
    $-2\frac{1}{3}$

6. $5\frac{4}{5}$
    $-2\frac{1}{4}$

7. $7\frac{15}{16} - 2\frac{4}{8}$

8. $6\frac{1}{3} - 4\frac{5}{6}$

9. $3\frac{1}{5} - 1\frac{9}{10}$

Write >, <, or = for each $\bigcirc$.

10. $7 - 3\frac{4}{9} \bigcirc 8\frac{1}{2} - 3\frac{1}{6}$

11. $9\frac{2}{5} - 1\frac{4}{6} \bigcirc 10 - 2\frac{4}{15}$

12. $6\frac{3}{8} - 5\frac{3}{4} \bigcirc 5\frac{1}{4} - 3\frac{5}{8}$

13. $8\frac{3}{4} - 3\frac{4}{5} \bigcirc 5\frac{1}{3} - 1\frac{5}{6}$

Spiral Review (Chapter 8, Lessons 3) **KEY** NS 2.3, MR 2.4

Add. Write the sum in simplest form.

14. $1\frac{1}{2} + 2\frac{1}{3}$

15. $4\frac{2}{7} + 3\frac{3}{7}$

16. $2\frac{1}{4} + 1\frac{5}{8}$

17. $8\frac{2}{3} + 5\frac{3}{4}$

18. $6\frac{3}{8} + 9\frac{1}{10}$

Name _____ Date _____

Subtract Mixed Numbers

CA Standards
KEY NS 2.3, NS 2.0

Solve problems 1–6. Write the difference in simplest form.

1. Janelle and Benjamin are measuring themselves in feet. Janelle is $5\frac{1}{3}$ feet tall. Benjamin is $5\frac{1}{2}$ feet tall. How much taller is Benjamin? Hint: Use 6 as a common denominator for the fractions.

   _____

2. Kendra is $4\frac{5}{6}$ feet tall. Her sister is $5\frac{2}{3}$ feet tall. How much taller is Kendra's sister?

   _____

3. Bud spent $17\frac{3}{4}$ hours at baseball practice this week. He spent $36\frac{1}{2}$ hours at school. How many more hours did he spend at school than at baseball practice?

   _____

4. Bart subtracted $8\frac{5}{7} - 4\frac{6}{7}$ and found $4\frac{6}{7}$. Explain what Bart's mistake was. Then tell the correct answer.

   _____

   _____

   _____

5. Chloe was writing a play to perform with her friends. In the play, the prince and princess had to escape from a tower, but their rope of knotted bed sheets was too short. If the tower was $57\frac{1}{4}$ feet tall and the rope was $52\frac{5}{18}$ feet long, how far would they have to jump? If they added to their rope by cutting that exact length off a 6-foot long sheet, how long would the leftover piece of sheet be?

   _____

   _____

   _____

6. The prince and princess in Chloe's play cut the new sheet and added to their rope of knotted sheets. They were disappointed to find that their rope was too short. Why? Give an example of possible lengths to illustrate your answer.

   _____

   _____

   _____

   _____

Problem Solving: Patterns in Tables

CA Standards
KEY NS 2.3, MR 2.3

Jessamyn makes belts in different lengths. The table shows the length of some of her belts with and without the buckles. If she makes a belt $36\frac{1}{2}$ inches long with the buckle, how long would it be without the buckle?

Jessamyn's Belts	
Length With Buckle (x)	Length Without Buckle (y)
$27\frac{7}{8}$ in	$26\frac{1}{4}$ in
30 in	$28\frac{3}{8}$ in
$34\frac{3}{8}$ in	$32\frac{3}{4}$ in
$39\frac{3}{4}$ in	$38\frac{1}{8}$ in

Look for a pattern by finding the difference between the lengths of belts with and without buckles.

$27\frac{7}{8}$ in $- 26\frac{1}{4}$ in $= 1\frac{5}{8}$ **in**
30 in $- 28\frac{3}{8}$ in $= 1\frac{5}{8}$ **in**
$34\frac{3}{8}$ in $- 32\frac{3}{4}$ in $= 1\frac{5}{8}$ **in**
$39\frac{3}{4}$ in $- 38\frac{1}{8}$ in $= 1\frac{5}{8}$ **in**

Use the pattern to write a function rule using the 2 variables: $x - 1\frac{5}{8} = y$

Use the function rule to answer the question:

$36\frac{1}{2} - 1\frac{5}{8} = 34\frac{7}{8}$

Solution: The length of the belt was $34\frac{7}{8}$ inches before the buckle was added.

Find a pattern. Write a function rule to solve.

1. Ethan's town has a train station. The table shows the length of each train's journey, with and without the stop. If a train takes $5\frac{11}{12}$ hours with the stop, how long would it take without the stop?

Length With stop (x)	Length Without stop (y)
$2\frac{2}{3}$	$2\frac{1}{2}$
$3\frac{5}{6}$	$3\frac{2}{3}$
$4\frac{3}{4}$	$4\frac{7}{12}$
$5\frac{1}{3}$	$5\frac{1}{6}$

_____

2. It takes a train $4\frac{1}{2}$ hours without a stop. How long is the length with a stop?

_____

Name _____ Date _____

Problem Solving: Patterns in Tables

Write a function rule to solve.

TABLE I		TABLE II		TABLE III	
Height of candle without holder (x)	**Height of candle with holder (y)**	**Weight of candy (c)**	**Weight of candy with wrapper (w)**	**Measure of peg (p)**	**Measure of slot (s)**
$6\frac{3}{4}$ in	$9\frac{1}{4}$ in	$\frac{3}{4}$ oz	$\frac{7}{8}$ oz	$9\frac{13}{16}$ mm	$8\frac{3}{4}$ mm
$6\frac{7}{8}$ in	$9\frac{3}{8}$ in	$1\frac{1}{8}$ oz	$1\frac{1}{4}$ oz	$10\frac{3}{8}$ mm	$9\frac{5}{16}$ mm
$7\frac{1}{2}$ in	10 in	$1\frac{3}{8}$ oz	$1\frac{1}{2}$ oz	$11\frac{3}{32}$ mm	$10\frac{1}{32}$ mm
$8\frac{1}{4}$ in	$10\frac{3}{4}$ in	$1\frac{1}{4}$ oz	$1\frac{3}{8}$ oz	$12\frac{1}{4}$ mm	$11\frac{3}{16}$ mm

For Problems 1–2, use Table I

1. If a candle is $8\frac{1}{2}$ inches tall, how tall will it be on the candle holder? Hint: Find the difference in height for each candle with and without the holder. Add that difference to $8\frac{1}{2}$.

_____

2. A new candle holder is $\frac{1}{2}$ inch shorter than the one used in the table. If a candle is $8\frac{1}{2}$ inches tall, how tall will it be on the new candle holder?

_____

For Problems 3–4, use Table II.

3. Chocolate wafers weigh $1\frac{5}{8}$ ounces. How much do they weigh with the wrapper?

_____

4. Peppermint frogs weigh $1\frac{1}{2}$ oz. How much do they weigh with the wrapper?

_____

For Problems 5–6, use Table III.

5. Eric uses wooden pegs to put together the furniture he builds. He always cuts the pegs slightly larger than the slots they fit into, so they will fit tightly. One of the pegs is $11\frac{7}{32}$ mm. What should be the measure of its slot?

_____

6. One of Eric's pegs is $8\frac{3}{32}$ mm. What should be the measure of its slot?

_____

Hands On: Multiply Whole Numbers and Fractions

CA Standard
NS 2.4

Find $2 \times \frac{3}{8}$.

Step ① Draw two squares and lightly shade them.

Step ② Draw lines to divide the squares into eighths. Shade $\frac{3}{8}$ of each square again.

Step ③ Count the number of eighths that are shaded twice.

Solution: $2 \times \frac{3}{8} = \frac{6}{8}$ or $\frac{3}{4}$

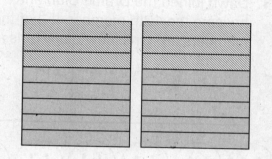

Write the answer in simplest form.

1.

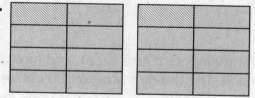

$2 \times \frac{1}{8} = $ _____

2.

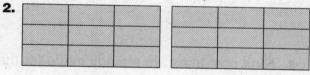

$2 \times \frac{5}{9} = $ _____

Use models to find each product. Write the answer in simplest form.

3. $4 \times \frac{1}{8} = $ _____   **4.** $5 \times \frac{7}{8} = $ _____   **5.** $8 \times \frac{5}{6} = $ _____   **6.** $6 \times \frac{3}{4} = $ _____

Spiral Review   (Chapter 8, Lesson 3 and Chapter 9, Lesson 4) **KEY** NS 2.3, NS 2.0

Find the sum or difference.

7. $3\frac{6}{7} + 1\frac{1}{2} = $ _____

8. $5\frac{4}{6} - 2\frac{2}{3} = $ _____

9. Mr. Henry has a board that is $6\frac{1}{2}$ feet long. He cuts off a piece that is $4\frac{3}{4}$ feet long. What is the length of the remaining piece?

Name _____ Date _____

Hands On: Multiply Whole Numbers and Fractions

CA Standard
NS 2.4

Use models to solve Problems 1–6.

1. Dawn joined the Drama Club and became the 12th member. If $\frac{5}{6}$ of the members are girls, how many girls are in the club?

2. The Drama Club is putting on a play. Eight members are working on scenery for the play. Of the 8 members, $\frac{2}{4}$ are painting the background. How many members are painting?

_____

3. Nine costumes are already made for the play. $\frac{2}{3}$ of those costumes are for the elves. How many elf costumes are already made?

4. The members take a break and have a snack. The director brought 20 cookies. Of those cookies, $\frac{3}{5}$ are sugar cookies. How many cookies are sugar?

_____

5. Tickets went on sale for the play. 145 tickets were sold. Of those tickets, $\frac{2}{5}$ were adult tickets. How many adult tickets were sold?

6. Using the information in question 5, how many children's tickets were sold? If the tickets for children cost $4 each, how much money did the play make from the sale of children's tickets?

_____

Name _____ Date _____

Multiply Fractions

CA Standards
NS 2.4, NS 2.5

Different Ways to Find $\frac{2}{3}$ of $\frac{6}{8}$

Way ① Multiply, then simplify.

$$\frac{2}{3} \times \frac{6}{8} = \frac{2 \times 6}{3 \times 8} = \frac{12}{24}$$

$$\frac{12}{24} \div \frac{12}{12} = \frac{1}{2}$$

Solution: $\frac{2}{3} \times \frac{6}{8} = \frac{1}{2}$

Way ② Simplify, then multiply.

$$\frac{2}{3} \times \frac{6}{8} = \frac{\overset{1}{2} \times \overset{2}{6}}{3 \times \underset{1}{2} \times \underset{1}{4}} = \frac{2}{4}$$

$$\frac{2 \div 2}{4 \div 2} = \frac{1}{2}$$

Multiply. Write your answer in simplest form.

1. $\frac{1}{6} \times \frac{2}{3} =$

2. $\frac{1}{8} \times 3 =$

3. $\frac{4}{9} \times \frac{3}{7} =$

4. $\frac{2}{5} \times \frac{3}{5} =$

5. $\frac{3}{4} \times \frac{5}{6} =$

6. $\frac{1}{10} \times 5 =$

7. $\frac{4}{7} \times \frac{1}{4} =$

8. $6 \times \frac{2}{3} =$

9. $12 \times \frac{2}{3} =$

10. $\frac{2}{5} \times \frac{1}{2} =$

11. $\frac{8}{9} \times \frac{4}{5} =$

12. $\frac{5}{6} \times 4 =$

Spiral Review (Chapter 8, Lesson 3 and Chapter 9, Lesson 4) **KEY** NS 2.3, NS 2.0

Find the sum or difference.

13. $8\frac{3}{5} + 3\frac{2}{10} =$ _____

14. $6\frac{9}{12} - 4\frac{1}{4} =$ _____

15. Sanjay spent $2\frac{1}{2}$ hours on Friday and $1\frac{3}{4}$ hours on Saturday planting flowers. How much time did he spend in all?

_____

Multiply Fractions

Solve. Show your work.

1. Kenny is buying 5 pizzas for LaToya's party. If the boys at the party eat $\frac{3}{5}$ of the pizzas, how many pizzas will the boys eat?

_____

2. LaToya is buying juice for her party. She wants to buy enough juice for each person to have $\frac{1}{2}$ liter. If 16 people are going to be at her party, how many liters of juice does LaToya need to buy?

_____

3. Elyssa is baking three different types of cookies for the party. She will make $\frac{5}{8}$ of them chocolate chip, and $\frac{2}{3}$ of those cookies will have nuts. What fraction of the cookies will be chocolate chip with nuts?

_____

4. Zack is bringing ice cream to the party. $\frac{2}{3}$ of the ice cream will be vanilla, and $\frac{1}{4}$ of the vanilla will have cookies mixed into it. What fraction of the ice cream will be vanilla with cookies?

_____

5. Jamal brings $\frac{3}{4}$ of the 8 cold sandwiches for the party and Jill brings $\frac{2}{3}$ of the 9 hot sandwiches. Who brings more sandwiches? Explain your answer.

_____

_____

_____

6. Cyndi makes 20 cupcakes. $\frac{4}{5}$ of the cupcakes are chocolate and $\frac{2}{8}$ of those have sprinkles. How many cupcakes are chocolate with sprinkles?

_____

_____

Name _____   Date _____

Multiply with Mixed Numbers

CA Standards
NS 2.4, NS 2.5

Find $3\frac{1}{3} \times \frac{3}{5}$.

Step 1 Write the mixed number as an improper fraction.

$$3\frac{1}{3} = \frac{10}{3}$$

Step 2 Use common factors to simplify. Then multiply.

$$\frac{10}{3} \times \frac{3}{5} = \frac{10 \times \overset{1}{\cancel{3}}}{\underset{1}{\cancel{3}} \times 5} = \frac{10 \times 1}{1 \times 5} = \frac{10}{5} = \frac{2}{1}$$

Step 3 Simplify.
$$\frac{2}{1} = 2$$

Solution: $3\frac{1}{3} \times \frac{3}{5} = 2$

Multiply. Write each product in simplest form.

1. $1\frac{1}{5} \times \frac{3}{4} =$

2. $2\frac{1}{8} \times \frac{1}{4} =$

3. $3\frac{1}{6} \times \frac{2}{5} =$

4. $\frac{4}{5} \times 2\frac{1}{2} =$

_____   _____   _____   _____

5. $1\frac{3}{8} \times \frac{4}{5} =$

6. $2\frac{1}{5} \times \frac{3}{7} =$

7. $3\frac{1}{4} \times \frac{8}{9} =$

8. $\frac{4}{7} \times 2\frac{3}{4} =$

_____   _____   _____   _____

9. $1\frac{2}{5} \times \frac{1}{4} =$

10. $\frac{1}{6} \times 3\frac{1}{3} =$

11. $\frac{5}{9} \times 3\frac{2}{3} =$

12. $5\frac{1}{2} \times \frac{4}{7}$

_____   _____   _____   _____

Spiral Review (Chapter 9, Lessons 2–4) **KEY** NS 2.3, NS 2.0

Subtract. Write your solution in simplest form.

13. $11 - 3\frac{2}{8} =$ _____

14. $4\frac{5}{9} - 3\frac{1}{3} =$ _____

15. Maria has $6\frac{1}{2}$ yards of fabric. She uses $1\frac{7}{8}$ yard to make a vest. How much fabric does she have left?

_____

Name _____ Date _____

Multiply with Mixed Numbers

CA Standards
NS 2.4, NS 2.5

Solve. Show your work

1. With her lunch, Susan got a super size cup holding $2\frac{2}{3}$ cups of milk. She was able to drink $\frac{2}{3}$ of the milk. How much milk did she drink?

   $\frac{8}{3} \times \frac{2}{3} =$ _____ cup

2. Jack is painting a picture in art class. A jar of blue paint holds $4\frac{7}{8}$ cups of paint. Jack uses $\frac{2}{5}$ of the jar. How much paint has Jack used?

   _____ cups

3. Debbie is painting a fence that is $8\frac{1}{4}$ times as wide as she is tall. If Debbie is $5\frac{1}{2}$ feet tall, how many feet wide is the fence?

   _____

   _____

4. Scott is a disc jockey at the local radio station. The current number one song is played 12 times each day. If the song is $4\frac{1}{5}$ minutes long, how many minutes a day is the song aired?

   _____

   _____

5. Terrance must decide which job offer to accept. One job pays $25 per hour for $37\frac{1}{2}$ hours each week and the other pays $825 per week regardless of how many hours he works. Which job should Terrance take?

   _____

   _____

   _____

6. Phil mows $6\frac{1}{2}$ acres of lawn each day. If he mows $\frac{2}{5}$ of the lawn before lunch, how many acres does he have to mow after lunch?

   _____

   _____

Hands On: Divide by a Unit Fraction

CA Standards
NS 2.4, NS 2.5

Find $9 \div \frac{1}{3}$.

Step 1 Draw 9 whole circles.

Step 2 Separate each circle into thirds.

Step 3 Count how many thirds are in 9 circles.

Solution: $9 \div \frac{1}{3} = 27$

Write the equation represented by each model. Write the answer in simplest form.

1.

_____

2.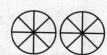

_____

3.

_____

4.

_____

Spiral Review (Chapter 5, Lesson 3) **KEY AF 1.2**

Write an algebraic expression for each word phrase. Use *n* to represent the unknown number.

5. 5 times a number

_____

6. 12 more than a number

_____

7. There are 35 students on each bus. Write an expression for the number of students on *n* buses.

_____

Name _____ Date _____

Hands On: Divide by a Unit Fraction

Use models to solve Problems 1–6.

1. Susan is making pizza dough for a party. She needs 3 cups of flour for each batch of dough. If she uses a $\frac{1}{2}$ cup to measure, how many $\frac{1}{2}$ cups will she need for a batch of dough?

   _____

   (1 cup)

2. Susan has another recipe that uses 4 cups of flour for each batch. If she uses a $\frac{1}{3}$ cup to measure, how many $\frac{1}{3}$ cups will she need for a batch?

   _____

   (1 cup)

3. Kevin has used Susan's dough to make 4 pizzas. He plans to serve each party guest $\frac{1}{8}$ of a pizza. How many people could he serve with 4 pizzas?

   _____

4. Cara is making apple pie for dessert. She plans on dividing the pies into fourths. How many people could she serve with 5 pies?

   _____

5. Frank is making punch for the party. He has 2 gallons of orange juice and plans to use $\frac{1}{2}$ quart for each batch of punch. If he wants to make 10 batches of punch, will he have enough? Explain. (Hint: there are 4 quarts in a gallon.)

   _____

   _____

   _____

6. Melanie is helping Kevin divide the pizzas. Melanie says that dividing 8 pizzas by $\frac{1}{4}$ would make the same number of pieces as dividing 4 pizzas by $\frac{1}{8}$. Is she right or wrong? Explain.

   _____

   _____

   _____

Divide Fractions by a Counting Number

CA Standards
NS 2.4, NS 2.5

Find $\frac{2}{3} \div 6$.

**Step ① ** Rewrite as a multiplication problem using the reciprocal of the divisor.

$$\frac{2}{3} \times \frac{1}{6}$$

**Step ② ** Find the product. Simplify if needed.

Solution: $\frac{2}{3} \times \frac{1}{6} = \frac{2}{18} = \frac{1}{9}$

Divide. Show your work. Simplify your answer.

1. $\frac{5}{8} \div 10 =$

2. $\frac{6}{10} \div 3 =$

3. $\frac{4}{5} \div 8 =$

4. $\frac{3}{7} \div 4 =$

_____   _____   _____   _____

5. $\frac{6}{5} \div 4 =$

6. $\frac{7}{9} \div 2 =$

7. $\frac{1}{2} \div 5 =$

8. $\frac{5}{6} \div 2 =$

_____   _____   _____   _____

9. $\frac{12}{5} \div 2 =$

10. $\frac{9}{10} \div 6 =$

11. $\frac{2}{5} \div 10 =$

12. $\frac{3}{4} \div 12 =$

_____   _____   _____   _____

Spiral Review   (Chapter 5, Lesson 3) **KEY AF 1.2**

**Write an algebraic expression for each word phrase.
Use *n* to represent the unknown number.**

13. 7 more than a number

14. 16 times a number

_____   _____

15. There are 42 students in Math Club. They are equally divided into
n teams for a competition. Write an expression for the number of
students on each team.

Name _____ Date _____

Divide Fractions by a Counting Number

CA Standards
NS 2.4, NS 2.5

Solve.

1. Ms. Hoffman owns $\frac{3}{4}$ of an acre of property. She decides to split her property into two equal lots to give to her two daughters. How many acres will each daughter receive? (Hint: $\frac{3}{4} \div \frac{2}{1} = \frac{3}{4} \times \frac{1}{2}$)

2. One of Ms. Hoffman's daughters wants to divide her lot into 3 equal parts, and plant birch trees on one part. How much of Ms. Hoffman's property will have birch trees? (Hint: In problem 1 you found the size of each daughter's lot.)

3. There are 5 children in the Grant family. They keep their toys in a closet in the family room. If $\frac{2}{3}$ of the closet is used for toys and the children split that space equally, what fraction of the closet space does each child have for toys?

4. The Grants' friends, the Haydens, have 4 children. In their closet, $\frac{3}{5}$ of the space is used for toys. If that space is shared equally by the children, how much space does each child have?

5. Four students are working on a 2-yard mural for their art fair. Each has already drawn on $\frac{3}{10}$ of a yard. They have divided the rest of the mural equally. How long is each student's remaining space on which to draw?

6. Gregory, Caroline, and Paige each brought $\frac{2}{3}$ of a box of candy to the movies. Their friends, Jack and Andrew, each brought $\frac{1}{2}$ of a box of candy. If all 5 friends split all the candy evenly, how much will each of them get?

Divide by a Fraction

CA Standards
NS 2.4, NS 2.5

Find $\frac{2}{3} \div \frac{6}{11}$.

Step 1 Rewrite as a multiplication problem using the reciprocal of the divisor.

$\frac{2}{3} \div \frac{6}{11} = \frac{2}{3} \times \frac{11}{6}$

Step 2 Find the product. Simplify if needed.

$\frac{2}{3} \times \frac{11}{6} = \frac{22}{18} = 1\frac{2}{9}$

Solution: $\frac{2}{3} \div \frac{6}{11} = 1\frac{2}{9}$

Divide. Write each answer in simplest form.

1. $15 \div \frac{2}{3} =$

2. $\frac{5}{8} \div \frac{5}{6} =$

3. $\frac{3}{4} \div \frac{1}{3} =$

4. $\frac{1}{2} \div \frac{7}{8} =$

5. $10 \div \frac{2}{5} =$

6. $9 \div \frac{2}{3} =$

7. $\frac{4}{5} \div \frac{1}{10} =$

8. $\frac{11}{12} \div \frac{1}{4} =$

9. $20 \div \frac{1}{2} =$

10. $\frac{1}{8} \div \frac{2}{7} =$

11. $\frac{3}{5} \div \frac{4}{7} =$

12. $5 \div \frac{1}{6} =$

Spiral Review (Chapter 8, Lesson 3) **KEY NS 2.3**

Add. Write each sum in simplest form.

13. $1\frac{2}{3} + 3\frac{1}{9} =$

14. $6\frac{1}{2} + 3\frac{3}{4} =$

15. Juan mixed $3\frac{3}{4}$ quarts of juice with $1\frac{1}{2}$ quarts of soda to make punch. How much punch did he make?

Divide by a Fraction

Solve.

1. Francesca has $12. If she exchanges the $12 for quarters, how many quarters will she receive? Hint: divide by $\frac{1}{4}$.

_____

2. Kevin has $15. If he exchanges his money for quarters, how many will he receive?

_____

3. Beth's garden is $\frac{8}{10}$ of an acre. She wants to use $\frac{1}{5}$ of an acre for each of her crops. How many crops can she plant?

_____

4. Paula said that $\frac{5}{8} \div \frac{1}{2}$ was equal to $\frac{5}{16}$. Explain Paula's mistake, then tell the correct answer in simplest form.

_____

_____

_____

_____

5. Evan had a piece of rope 48 inches long. He gave $\frac{2}{3}$ of a foot to each of his friends. How many friends received rope from Evan?

_____

6. Alex makes two identical pizzas for his brother's birthday party. He uses the same amount of each ingredient on each pizza. Alex uses $\frac{5}{6}$ of a cup of cheese on $\frac{3}{4}$ of the first pizza. At this rate, how many cups of cheese will he put on the second pizza?

_____

Name _____ Date _____

Divide with Mixed Numbers

Find $3\frac{1}{3} \div 1\frac{1}{2}$.

Step ❶ Write the mixed numbers as improper fractions.

$$3\frac{1}{3} \div 1\frac{1}{2} = \frac{10}{3} \div \frac{3}{2}$$

Step ❷ Rewrite as a multiplication problem using the reciprocal of the divisor.

$$\frac{10}{3} \times \frac{2}{3}$$

Step ❸ Multiply. Simplify if needed.

$$\frac{10}{3} \times \frac{2}{3} = \frac{20}{9} = 2\frac{2}{9}$$

Divide. Write each quotient in simplest form.

1. $\frac{1}{3} \div 2\frac{1}{3} =$

2. $\frac{5}{6} \div 1\frac{5}{6} =$

3. $\frac{1}{2} \div 3\frac{1}{4} =$

4. $1\frac{2}{5} \div 1\frac{3}{5} =$

_____

_____

_____

_____

5. $\frac{1}{5} \div 3\frac{4}{5} =$

6. $\frac{2}{3} \div 1\frac{1}{9} =$

7. $\frac{3}{4} \div 1\frac{1}{2} =$

8. $2\frac{1}{3} \div 1\frac{1}{6} =$

_____

_____

_____

_____

9. $\frac{7}{8} \div 2\frac{3}{4} =$

10. $\frac{5}{7} \div 2\frac{1}{2} =$

11. $\frac{3}{5} \div 3\frac{1}{5} =$

12. $\frac{4}{9} \div 5\frac{1}{3} =$

_____

_____

_____

_____

Spiral Review (Chapter 10, Lessons 2 and 3) **NS 2.5**

Solve. Write the product in simplest form.

13. $2\frac{1}{2} \times 1\frac{1}{3} =$

14. $\frac{4}{5} \times \frac{7}{8} =$

_____

_____

15. The debate team ate $\frac{5}{8}$ of a package of cookies at a meeting. If there are 40 cookies in the package, how many did they eat?

_____

Use with text pp. 236–239

Name _____ Date _____

Divide with Mixed Numbers

CA Standards
NS 2.4, NS 2.5

Solve.

1. Don's round-trip train commute takes $2\frac{1}{2}$ hours each day. If the train takes the same amount of time in each direction, how many hours is a one-way trip? (Hint: change $2\frac{1}{2}$ to $\frac{5}{2}$, then divide by 2.)

_____

2. Mr. Gittens spent $9\frac{3}{4}$ hours commuting last week. If he commuted $3\frac{1}{4}$ hours each day, how many days did Mr. Gittens commute? (Hint: change the mixed numbers to improper fractions, then divide $\frac{39}{4} \div \frac{13}{4}$ to find the number of days.)

_____

3. Tracey is in school for $6\frac{2}{3}$ hours each day. Each class lasts $\frac{5}{6}$ of an hour. How many classes does Tracey have each day?

_____

4. On Wednesday, Tracey's school has workshop classes, which last $1\frac{1}{3}$ hours. How many classes does she have on Wednesdays?

_____

5. Kathleen measured her pencil and found that it was $3\frac{1}{2}$ inches long. She then measured it again and counted the $\frac{1}{8}$s of an inch. She got 28. Was she correct? Explain.

_____

6. This week Nicole studied every night from Monday through Friday, for a total of $6\frac{1}{2}$ hours. On Monday, she studied for $1\frac{1}{4}$ hours. She studied for the same number of hours each night from Tuesday through Friday. How many hours did she study on Friday night?

_____

100

Problem Solving: Reasonable Answers

Example 1 Sometimes answers are unreasonable because the problem is misinterpreted.

Jake has $3\frac{1}{2}$ feet of wood and uses $\frac{1}{3}$ foot for each model he makes. He thinks he will be able to make only 2 models.

His answer is unreasonable. If he uses $\frac{1}{3}$ of a foot in each model, he will be able to make many more than 2.

Example 2 Sometimes an answer does not make sense.

Sophie has $5\frac{1}{2}$ pints of lemonade to divide among her friends. She plans to give $1\frac{1}{2}$ pints to each friend. She thinks she will be able to give lemonade to $3\frac{2}{3}$ friends.

Her answer is unreasonable because you cannot have $\frac{2}{3}$ of a friend.

Tell whether each underlined statement is reasonable or unreasonable. Then solve.

1. Leah has 32 animals in her collection of toy dogs and cats. Ten of these are cats. So, exactly $\frac{1}{2}$ of the animals are dogs.

   _____

2. Bridget has $3\frac{1}{2}$ tubes of paint. She uses $\frac{1}{8}$ of a tube on each picture she paints. This means she can paint 4 pictures.

   _____

3. Lars planted a rosebush $4\frac{2}{3}$ yards away from his house. He planted a second rosebush $\frac{1}{4}$ as far from his house. So, the second rosebush was planted a little over a yard from his house.

   _____

Spiral Review (Chapter 10, Lesson 3) NS 2.4, NS 2.5

Solve. Write the product in simplest form.

4. $1\frac{1}{4} \times 1\frac{2}{5} =$

5. $2\frac{2}{3} \times 6\frac{5}{8} =$

6. Shannon has $2\frac{1}{4}$ cups of flour and uses $\frac{1}{2}$ of it. How much flour does she use?

   _____

Problem Solving: Reasonable Answers

Tell whether each underlined statement is reasonable or unreasonable. Then solve.

1. Barry puts TVs on a 15-foot shelf in his electronics store. He allows $2\frac{1}{2}$ feet of space for each TV. <u>He will be able to put 5.5 TVs on the shelf.</u>

   _____

   _____

2. Jessica used different kinds of juice to make 5 quarts of punch. She used $1\frac{1}{4}$ quart of each kind of juice. <u>So, she used 4 kinds of juice.</u>

   _____

   _____

3. Kendall did 5 pages of homework in $\frac{3}{4}$ hour. She spent the same amount of time on each page. <u>So, she spent $3\frac{3}{4}$ hours on each page.</u>

   _____

   _____

4. Tomas needed equal-sized pieces of plywood. He was able to cut $3\frac{1}{3}$ pieces of the size he needed out of $2\frac{1}{2}$ feet of wood. <u>So, each full piece was $\frac{3}{4}$ foot long.</u>

   _____

   _____

5. Teri had two carpentry jobs to complete, and expected them each to take the same amount of time. She spent $1\frac{1}{2}$ hours doing $\frac{4}{5}$ of the first job. <u>Teri decided that working at the same rate she could do the second job in 1 hour and 12 minutes.</u>

   _____

   _____

   _____

6. Mike had $16\frac{3}{4}$ pages to read for his history assignment. He read $\frac{1}{2}$ of the pages on Monday and $\frac{1}{4}$ of what was left on Tuesday. <u>He had about 6 pages left to read on Wednesday.</u>

   _____

   _____

   _____

Hands On: Add and Subtract Decimals

CA Standards
KEY NS 2.1, MR 2.3

Use models to find the sum or difference.

Example 1: $4.60
        + 0.75

Solution: $5.35

Example 2: $6.13
        − 3.65

Solution: $2.48

Use models to add or subtract.

1.   1.08
   +36.94

2. $12.42
   + 9.79

3.   12.3
   − 4.07

4.   26.04
   − 0.005

Spiral Review (Chapter 9, Lessons 2 and 3) **KEY** NS 2.3, NS 2.0

Subtract. Write each answer in simplest form.

5. $24\frac{5}{12} - 16\frac{5}{12} =$ _____

6. $54\frac{6}{16} - 37\frac{4}{16} =$ _____

7. Mike jogged $4\frac{7}{10}$ of a mile. Jimmy jogged $6\frac{9}{10}$ of a mile.
   How much further did Jimmy jog than Mike?

_____

Hands On: Add and Subtract Decimals

CA Standards
KEY NS 2.1, MR 2.3

Use models to find the sums or differences.

1. Ross makes $12.50 per hour at his job at the bakery. If he gets a raise of $1.45 per hour, how much will Ross make per hour?

_____

2. Ross worked 37.25 hours last week and 32.25 hours this week. How many more hours did Ross work last week than this week?

_____

3. Tyler bought groceries for $35.23. He gave the cashier a $50 dollar bill. How much change should he receive?

_____

4. Abigail and Anna run track for their middle school track team. Recently they competed in a one-mile race. Abigail finished the mile in 9.527 minutes and Anna finished in 7.988 minutes. Who finished the race first? By how many minutes?

_____

5. Brittany bought a CD for $13.65, a new pair of headphones for $6.79, and a book for $9.29. How much did Brittany spend altogether at the store?

_____

6. Everett received a $50 gift card for his birthday. Everett purchased a remote controlled car for $19.99; and a puzzle for $3.37. How much money is left on Everett's gift card?

_____

Estimate Sums and Differences

CA Standards
KEY NS 2.1, MR 2.5

Ways to Estimate 8.217 − 3.5	
Way 1 Round each number to the nearest tenth. $\quad$ 8.217 $\qquad$ 1 < 5 so round to 8.2 $-$ 3.5 $\qquad$ 0 < 5 so round to 3.5 Subtract. $\quad$ 8.2 $-$ 3.5 $\overline{\quad 4.7}$ **Solution:** 4.7	**Way 2** Round each number to the nearest whole number. $\quad$ 8.217 $\qquad$ 2 < 5 so round to 8 $-$ 3.5 $\qquad$ 5 = 5 so round to 4 Subtract. $\quad$ 8 $-$ 4 $\overline{\quad 4}$ **Solution:** 4

Estimate the sum or difference by rounding each number to the nearest tenth. Check that your answer is reasonable.

1. $0.548 + 0.356 =$ $\qquad$ **2.** $0.721 + 0.894 =$ $\qquad$ **3.** $0.155 + 0.426 =$ $\qquad$ **4.** $0.659 + 0.121 =$

_____ _____ _____ _____

5. $0.793 - 0.518 =$ $\qquad$ **6.** $0.409 - 0.316 =$ $\qquad$ **7.** $0.564 - 0.293 =$ $\qquad$ **8.** $0.917 - 0.462 =$

_____ _____ _____ _____

Estimate the sum or difference by rounding each number to the nearest whole number. Check that your answer is reasonable.

9. $5.167 + 7.805 =$ $\qquad$ **10.** $21.853 + 6.339 =$ $\qquad$ **11.** $3.056 + 41.749 =$ $\qquad$ **12.** $16.084 + 7.402 =$

_____ _____ _____ _____

13. $62.995 - 45.130 =$ **14.** $17.622 - 13.296 =$ **15.** $31.505 - 19.189 =$ **16.** $4.263 - 0.978 =$

_____ _____ _____ _____

Spiral Review (Chapter 9, Lessons 2 and 3) **KEY NS 2.3, NS 2.0**

Subtract. Write each answer in simplest form.

17. $18 - 6\frac{3}{4} =$ _____ **18.** $35\frac{7}{8} - 16\frac{3}{8} =$ _____

19. Heather and Madison participated in a cookie-eating contest. Heather ate $23\frac{3}{6}$ cookies. Madison ate $35\frac{5}{6}$. How many more cookies did Madison eat than Heather?

Name _____ Date _____

Estimate Sums and Differences

CA Standards
KEY NS 2.1, MR 2.5

Use the data from the chart to solve Problems 1–6.

Average Annual Precipitation of 5 U.S. Cities	
City	Average Annual Precipitation (in inches)
Mobile, Alabama	63.96
Chicago, Illinois	35.82
Miami, Florida	55.91
Memphis, Tennessee	52.10
Raleigh, North Carolina	41.43

1. Estimate how many more inches of precipitation Mobile averages than Chicago to the nearest inch.

   _____

2. Estimate how many more inches of precipitation Miami averages than Raleigh to the nearest tenth.
   55.9̲1 → _____ 41.4̲3 → _____

   _____

3. Estimate how many more inches of precipitation Mobile averages than Chicago to the nearest tenth of an inch.

   _____

4. Estimate which two cities have a greater annual precipitation; Mobile and Chicago or Miami and Memphis?

   _____

5. Which two cities when rounded to the nearest tenth have a total average annual precipitation of 77.2 inches?

   _____

6. If you were estimating the total precipitation for all the cities in the chart, would it make sense to round each number to the nearest ten inches? Explain why or why not.

   _____

   _____

   _____

   _____

Add and Subtract Decimals

CA Standards
KEY NS 2.1, MR 2.1

In a recent Swimming Grand Prix, Michael Phelps finished with a time of 45.90 seconds in the 100yd back stroke race, ahead of Peter Marshall and Aaron Peirsol who finished with times of 46.28 seconds and 46.79 seconds. What is the difference in time between Michael Phelps' score and Aaron Peirsol's score?

Step ① Align the decimal points. Subtract the hundredths.	**Step ② ** Subtract the tenths. 7 < 9, so regroup 1 one as 10 tenths.	**Step ③ ** Subtract the ones. Write the decimal point in the answer.	**Solution:** The difference in time between Michael Phelps' score and Aaron Peirsol's score is 0.89 seconds.	**Check by estimating.** 46.79 rounds to 47.
46.79 − 45.90 _____ 9	5 17 ~~46.79~~ − 45.90 _____ 89	5 17 ~~46.79~~ − 45.90 _____ 0.89		45.90 rounds to 46. 47 − 46 = 1 0.89 is close to 1, so my answer is reasonable.

Add or subtract.

1. 50.87
   + 43.95

2. 89.14
   + 63.82

3. 41.948
   + 8.655

4. 57.209
   + 25.863

5. 86.8
   − 59.9

6. 4.000
   − 2.731

7. 84.306
   − 55.704

8. 10.000
   − 3.529

Spiral Review (Chapter 9, Lesson 2) **KEY** NS 2.3, NS 2.0

Simplify.

9. $7 - \frac{1}{6} =$ _____

10. $3 - \frac{3}{4} =$ _____

11. Shawn had a pizza party for his birthday. His mom ordered 5 pizzas for the party. Shawn's guests ate all of the pizza except $\frac{3}{8}$ of the last pizza. How many pizzas did he and his friends eat?

_____

Add and Subtract Decimals

CA Standards
KEY NS 2.1, MR 2.1

Use the table below to answer questions 1–6.

White Marlin Open Fishing Tournament		
Fish Category	**Boat Name**	**Fish Weight**
Tuna	Sunshine 1	80.57
Tuna	Mr. Spot	115.03
Tuna	Ocean 7	42.51
Marlin	Sunshine 1	55.79
Marlin	Guppy	63.58
Marlin	Spinnaker	74.36

1. What is the total weight of the tuna caught on the Sunshine 1 and Mr. Spot boats?

$$115.03$$
$$+\ 80.57$$

_____

2. What is the difference in weight between the Marlin caught on the Guppy and the Tuna caught on Ocean 7?

$$63.58$$
$$-\ 42.51$$

_____

3. How much heavier is the total catch of tuna than the total catch of marlin?

_____

4. What is the difference in weight between the largest tuna and the largest marlin? The smallest tuna and the smallest marlin?

_____

5. Two fish weigh a total of 106.09 lb. Which two boats brought these fish in?

_____

6. Fish from the Guppy and Spinnaker boats weigh a total of 137.94 lb. How much more weight was this than the total weight brought in by Sunshine 1?

_____

Hands On: Multiply Decimals

CA Standards
KEY NS 2.1, MR 2.3

Find 2 × 0.78.

Step 1 Use two hundredths models. Shade 0.78 blue. Then shade 0.78 red.

Solution: $2 \times 0.78 = 1.56$.

 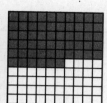

Step 2 Count the shaded hundredths. There are $0.78 + 0.78$, or 156 shaded hundredths. The number 156 hundredths can be written as 1 whole and 56 hundredths, or 1.56.

Use models to multiply. Write each product as a decimal.

1. $0.3 \times 0.7 =$ _____

2. $0.9 \times 0.6 =$ _____

3. $0.6 \times 0.6 =$ _____

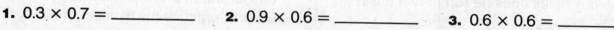

4. $0.8 \times 0.9 =$ _____

5. $3.1 \times 0.4 =$ _____

6. $1.4 \times 0.8 =$ _____

 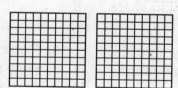 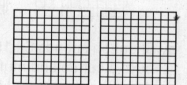

Spiral Review (Chapter 6, Lesson 3) **KEY AF 1.2**

Write the name of the property that matches each equation.

7. $w + 4 = 4 + w$ _____

8. $y + 0 = y$ _____

9. Jack had this homework problem: $(7 + h) + 5 = 7 + (h + 5)$. He is unsure what property matches the equation. Write the property.

_____

Homework

109

Use with text pp. 270–271

Name _____ Date _____

Hands On: Multiply Decimals

CA Standards
KEY NS 2.1, MR 2.3

Solve. In 1–4, use grids to help solve.

1. Rosa lives 0.4 kilometers from school. How many kilometers does Rosa walk each day to and from school?

2. Kim spends $0.60 on a juice for her lunch. Kim also buys a juice for her friend. How much money does Kim spend on juice?

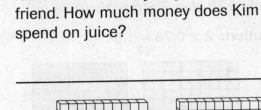

_____

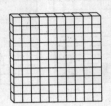

3. Lennie runs 1.1 miles each day. How many miles does he run in two days?

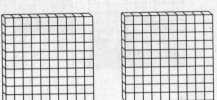

4. Edward practices his trumpet each day for 0.3 of an hour. How long did Edward practice his trumpet after three days?

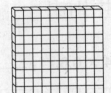 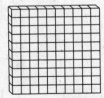

5. Shannon spends $4.15 every time she buys a coffee and muffin. How much does Shannon spend in five days on coffee and muffins?

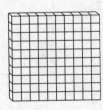

6. Garrett reads 2.8 pages in 3.5 minutes. How much does Garrett read in 31.5 minutes?

_____

Multiply Whole Numbers and Decimals

CA Standard
KEY NS 2.1

Find 1.89 × 4.

**Step ① ** Multiply. Ignore the decimal point.

$$\begin{array}{r} 1.89 \\ \times\ 4 \\ \hline 756 \end{array}$$

Step ② Place the decimal point in the product.

$$\begin{array}{r} 1.89 \longrightarrow \quad 2 \text{ decimal places} \\ \times\ 4 \longrightarrow +\ 0 \text{ decimal places} \\ \hline 756 \qquad\quad 2 \text{ decimal places} \end{array}$$

$$\begin{array}{r} 1.89 \\ \times\ 4 \\ \hline 7.56 \end{array}$$

Solution: The product of 1.89 × 4 is 7.56

Find each product.

1. $5 \times 2.2 =$

2. $3 \times 0.12 =$

3. $2.75 \times 7 =$

_____

_____

_____

4. $12.5 \times 4 =$

5. $8 \times 4.2 =$

6. $14.1 \times 2 =$

_____

_____

_____

7. $7.6 \times 3 =$

8. $9 \times 3.9 =$

9. $5.2 \times 7 =$

_____

_____

_____

Spiral Review (Chapter 6, Lesson 3) **KEY** AF 1.2

Write the name of the property that matches each equation.

10. $6 + (21 + b) = (6 + 21) + b$

11. $7 + p = p + 7$

_____

_____

12. Jason said any number plus zero equals that number.
What property is Jason talking about?

_____

Multiply Whole Numbers and Decimals

CA Standard
KEY NS 2.1

Use the data in the table to solve the following problems.

Joe's Gems		
Employee	**Hours per Week**	**Pay per Hour**
Rosa	30	$8.25
Leah	25	$9.50
Marcus	40	$12.35
Overtime pay is twice the regular pay.		

1. How much money does Rosa earn each week? Hint: Count the number of decimal places in the factors to place the decimal point in the product.

_____

2. Suppose Joe hired another employee who worked 10 hours each week at $8.15 per hour. What would this employee earn in one week?

_____

3. Who earns more money each week, Rosa or Leah? What is the difference in their pay?

_____

_____

_____

_____

4. As the owner, Joe works 45 hours per week. His hourly rate is $25.25. How much money does Joe earn each week?

_____

5. Leah would like to earn $300 next week. She has agreed to work extra hours. How many extra hours of overtime pay will Leah need to work to earn at least $300?

_____

6. Marcus was promoted to manager and received a raise of $1.50 per hour. If he works the same number of hours as he did before the promotion, how much more money will he earn each week?

_____

Estimate Products

CA Standards
KEY NS 2.1, NS 1.1

Ways to Estimate 228 × 0.77		
Round to higher numbers.	**Round to lesser numbers.**	**Use fractions.**
228 rounds to 300	228 rounds to 200	228 is about 200
0.77 rounds to 0.8	0.77 rounds to 0.7	0.77 is about $\frac{3}{4}$
Solution: $300 \times 0.8 = 240$	**Solution:** $200 \times 0.7 = 140$	**Solution:** $\frac{3}{4}$ of 200 is 150

Estimate each product. Write an equation to show the rounded numbers you used.

1. $13 \times 0.47 =$

2. $5.96 \times 3 =$

3. $4 \times 2.89 =$

_____ _____ _____

4. $3 \times 3.98 =$

5. $9.87 \times 12 =$

6. $3.075 \times 15 =$

_____ _____ _____

7. $4.46 \times 3 =$

8. $1.52 \times 23 =$

9. $5 \times 3.7 =$

_____ _____ _____

Spiral Review (Chapter 9, Lessons 2 and 4) **KEY** NS 2.3

Solve. Express your answers in simplest form.

10. $5 - 3\frac{1}{2} =$ _____

11. $7\frac{3}{5} - 2\frac{2}{4} =$ _____

12. YuMin has $10\frac{1}{2}$ cups of sugar in a container. She needs $1\frac{3}{4}$ cups of sugar to make a cake and $7\frac{1}{3}$ cups of sugar to make peach jam. After making both the cake and the jam, how much sugar is left?

_____

Name _____ Date _____

Estimate Products

CA Standards
KEY NS 2.1, NS 1.1

Use the information in the table to answer the questions.

Price of Orchestra Instruments			
Cello	$1,769.95	Flute	$2,459
Clarinet	$925.01	Violin	$1,050.49
French horn	$7,795.01	Harmonica	$75.99

1. About how much is the cost of 6 clarinets?

900 × 6 = _____

_____

2. The orchestra needs 3 harmonicas. Will $200 cover the cost of the harmonicas? Explain your answer.

_____

_____

_____

_____

3. About how much money would the orchestra spend to buy 15 violins?

_____

_____

4. Maria said that 5 clarinets would cost about $5,000. Bill said the cost is about $4,500. Who is correct? Explain.

_____

_____

_____

_____

5. The orchestra would like to purchase 3 French horns and 5 flutes. What is the estimated cost of these items?

_____

6. The director of the orchestra plays the cello, violin, and the harmonica. About how much would she spend if she were to buy all three instruments?

_____

Name _____ Date _____

Multiply Decimals

Find 0.7 × 0.3.

Step ① Multiply. Ignore the decimal points.	**Step ②** Place the decimal point in the product.	
$\begin{array}{r} 7 \\ \times\,3 \\ \hline 21 \end{array}$	$\begin{array}{r} 0.7 \\ \times\,0.3 \\ \hline 0.21 \end{array}$	1 decimal place 1 decimal place 2 decimal places

Multiply.

1. $0.7 \times 0.2 =$ _____   **2.** $0.9 \times 0.3 =$ _____   **3.** $0.32 \times 0.5 =$ _____

4. $0.3 \times 6.2 =$ _____   **5.** $1.25 \times 4.7 =$ _____   **6.** $0.6 \times 5.4 =$ _____

7. $2.65 \times 0.29 =$ _____   **8.** $1.52 \times 23 =$ _____   **9.** $1.57 \times 6.6 =$ _____

Compare. Write >, <, or =.

10. 0.4×6.1 ◯ 12.2×0.2 **11.** 3.5×1.7 ◯ 4.6×1.8

12. 0.9×5.6 ◯ 2.2×1.7 **13.** 0.4×3.8 ◯ 7.6×0.2

Spiral Review (Chapter 10, Lessons 1 and 2) **NS 2.4, NS 2.5**

Complete each multiplication sentence.

14. $\frac{3}{5} \times \frac{3}{7} =$ _____   **15.** $25 \times \frac{4}{5} =$ _____

16. At the Convenience Corner store, the manager ordered 12 cases of candy. Each case weighed $5\frac{3}{4}$ pounds. How many pounds of candy did the manager order? Show your work.

_____

Name _____ Date _____

Multiply Decimals

CA Standard
KEY NS 2.1

Solve.

1. The average rainfall in San Francisco during January is 4.45 inches. If San Francisco were to receive only 0.5 of the average amount of rain, how much rain would the city receive?

    4.45 × 0.5

    _____

2. Buffalo, New York, is known for the snowfall it receives every year. During the months of November, December, and January, the average snowfall is 10.88 inches. If it snows 2.5 times the average, how much snow will Buffalo receive?

    _____

3. Miami, Florida, receives an average of 8.63 inches of rain each August. If it only rains 0.8 of the average amount next August, how much rain will Miami receive?

    _____

4. Phoenix, Arizona, is one of the driest cities in the United States. It receives just 8.29 inches of rain each year. If Phoenix receives the same amount of rain each month, how much rain will it get in 1.5 years?

    _____

5. Duluth, Minnesota, has a mean yearly precipitation of 21 inches. San Diego, California, has a mean yearly precipitation that is 0.345 of Duluth's. What is San Diego's mean yearly precipitation?

    _____

6. Indianapolis, Indiana, receives an average of 40.94 inches of precipitation each year. To find the mean precipitation for one-fourth of the year in Indianapolis, would you multiply by 0.25 or $\frac{1}{4}$? Explain.

    _____

    _____

    _____

    _____

Name _____   Date _____

Zeros in the Product

CA Standards
KEY NS 2.1, MR 2.1

Find 0.02 × 0.04.

Step 1 Multiply. Ignore the decimal points.	**Step 2** Place the decimal point in the product.
$\begin{array}{r} 0.02 \\ \times\ 0.04 \\ \hline 8 \end{array}$	$\begin{array}{r} 0.02 \\ \times\ 0.04 \\ \hline 0.0008 \end{array}$ 2 decimal places 2 decimal places 4 decimal places

Multiply.

1. $\begin{array}{r} 0.07 \\ \times\ 0.2 \\ \hline \end{array}$

2. $\begin{array}{r} 0.03 \\ \times\ 0.9 \\ \hline \end{array}$

3. $\begin{array}{r} 0.005 \\ \times\ 0.3 \\ \hline \end{array}$

4. $\begin{array}{r} 0.002 \\ \times\ 0.08 \\ \hline \end{array}$

5. $\begin{array}{r} 0.006 \\ \times\ 0.09 \\ \hline \end{array}$

6. $\begin{array}{r} 0.025 \\ \times\ 0.7 \\ \hline \end{array}$

7. $\begin{array}{r} 0.04 \\ \times\ 0.01 \\ \hline \end{array}$

8. $\begin{array}{r} 0.03 \\ \times\ 0.5 \\ \hline \end{array}$

9. $0.051 \times 0.06 =$

10. $0.009 \times 0.04 =$

11. $0.08 \times 0.005 =$

12. $0.6 \times 0.001 =$

Spiral Review (Chapter 12, Lesson 2) **KEY** NS 2.1

Round each number to the nearest tenth to estimate the sum or difference.

13. $1.43 + 0.079 + 13.1 =$ _____

14. $123.45 - 72.106 =$ _____

15. Evan has $20. He would like to buy a CD for $13.69 and a DVD for $6.50. Before tax is added, will Evan have enough money to purchase both items? Explain your reasoning using what you know about estimating and adding decimals.

_____

_____

_____

Name _____ Date _____

Zeros in the Product

CA Standards
KEY NS 2.1, MR 2.1

To solve Problems 1 and 2, use the Maryland sales tax of 5%.

1. The cost of a candy bar is $0.89. How much sales tax will be charged on the candy bar? Hint: Remember to add a zero if necessary.

_____

2. Paul's Pizza is having a sale on Mozza-Melts. Each order of Mozza-Melts costs $0.99. Including tax, how much will a customer pay for one order of Mozza-Melts?

_____

To solve Problems 3 and 4, use the California sales tax of 6%

3. Chris bought 17 pieces of candy for $0.05 each. Including tax, how much did Chris pay for the candy?

_____

4. Ken bought 15 pencils for $0.12 each. What was the total amount of money Ken paid for the pencils?

_____

To solve Problems 5 and 6, use the Puerto Rico sales tax of 5.5% for all items purchased, and add on another 15% for personal items.

5. Kim and Erica went on vacation in Puerto Rico. While there, Kim bought a straw hat for $1.49 at a market. Including tax, how much did Kim pay for the hat?

_____

6. Erica chose to buy a braided bracelet for $1.79 at the market. What was Erica's total cost for the bracelet?

_____

Name _____ Date _____

Problem Solving: Estimate or Exact?

Use the table to solve.

The library staff is raising money to buy chairs for the new children's section. They need to raise $1,200 by July. How much money have they raised so far? How much money do they still need in order to reach their goal?

Money Raised	
Month	**Amount**
March	$380
April	$295
May	$210
June	$200

Find an Exact Answer

Add the amounts raised in each month.

```
  380
  295
  210
+ 200
-----
1,085
```

The library has raised exactly $1,085.

Use an Estimate

Round the amounts to the nearest hundred.

```
  400
  300
  200
+ 200
-----
1,100
```

The library has raised about $1,100.

Solve Using an Estimate

Subtract the estimated total from the total amount the library needs.

```
  1,200
- 1,100
-------
    100
```

The library needs to raise about $100 more to reach their goal.

1. The table to the right shows how much money the Morris family spent at the circus. Exactly how much money did they spend in all? _____

2. About how much money did the Morris family spend on tickets and popcorn?
_____

3. Mr. Morris brought $100 to the circus. Exactly how much money does he have left? _____

Trip to the Circus	
Item	**Amount Spent**
tickets	$45
popcorn	$12
souvenirs	$19
drinks	$10

Spiral Review (Chapter 10, Lesson 1) **NS 2.4**

Complete each multiplication sentence.

4. $\frac{3}{4} \times$ _____ $= 24$

5. $\frac{2}{5} \times$ _____ $= 4$

6. Alex needs 2 cups of milk to make pancakes. He only has a $\frac{1}{3}$ measuring cup. In order to reach 2 cups of milk, how many times does Alex need to fill the measuring cup?
$\frac{1}{3}$ cup $\times$ _____ $= 2$ cups

Name _____ Date _____

Problem Solving: Estimate or Exact?

Solve. Explain why your answer makes sense.

1. Jeremy needs to buy a new car. The prices of several cars are listed in the table below. About how much more is Car 1 than Car 3? HINT: Round the price of Car 1 to the nearest thousand, then round the price of Car 3. Subtract.

Car Prices	
Car 1	$24,530
Car 2	$26,545
Car 3	$23,650

_____

_____

2. The table below shows the weight of Aunt Maria's baby. Exactly how much weight did the baby gain in 2 weeks? HINT: Subtract the weight at birth from the weight at 2 weeks.

Baby's Weight	
at birth	7 lbs. 4 oz.
at 2 weeks	7 lbs. 9 oz.

_____

_____

_____

3. A restaurant records the amount of food and drinks sold each year. Each hot chocolate costs $2. How much money did the restaurant make selling hot chocolate in 2005?

Food and Drinks Sold in 2005	
Cookies	12,643
Apple cider	3,776
Hot chocolate	63,824
Sandwiches	39,715

_____

_____

4. Use the table of Food and Drinks Sold in 2005 from problem 3. About how many more sandwiches were sold than cookies?

_____

_____

_____

5. The table below shows exactly how much Mr. Rodriquez spent last year on business trips. His company will cover 80% of his expenses. How much is not covered by his company?

Business Expenses	
Hotel	$21,924.50
Taxis	$1,516.90
Food	$14,723.75

6. Kelly made a table of her scores on Science tests this semester. What was her average score, to the nearest whole number?

Scores on Science Tests	
Test 1	83.8%
Test 2	91.7%
Test 3	85.2%
Test 4	94.2%

120

Hands On: Division with Decimals

Divide 3 ÷ 0.6. Use tenths models to divide.

Step 1 Model 3. Use 3 whole tenths models.

Step 2 The divisor is 0.6. The divisor will represent the number of objects in each group. Seperate both models into tenths. Then make as many equal groups as possible with 6 tenths in each group.

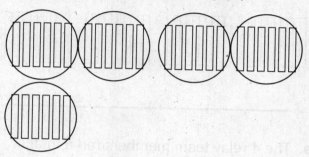

Step 3 Count the number of groups.

Step 4 Write a division equation to show your answer.

Solution: 3 ÷ 0.6 = 5

Use tenths models to divide. Check your answers by multiplying.

1. 4 ÷ 0.4 = _____

2. 2.4 ÷ 0.6 = _____

3. 0.9 ÷ 0.3 = _____

4. 5 ÷ 0.1 = _____

5. 6 ÷ 1.5 = _____

6. 3 ÷ 1.2 = _____

7. 2.2 ÷ 0.2 = _____

8. 0.8 ÷ 0.4 = _____

Spiral Review (Chapter 5, Lesson 2) **NS 1.3**

Simplify.

9. (12 + 6) − 8 = _____

10. (6 − 3) + 15 = _____

11. Karen spent $7 on a movie ticket and $4 on popcorn. If Karen had a $3-off coupon for the ticket, how much did Karen spend?

_____

Homework

121

Use with text pp. 294–295

Hands On: Division with Decimals

CA Standards
KEY NS 2.1, **KEY** NS 2.2

Solve.

1. For an afternoon snack, 4 cupcakes were divided into 0.5. How many cupcake halves are there now for snack? Use tenths models to divide.

$4 \div 0.5 = n$

_____

2. Two candy bars were also for snack time. If each bar was divided into 0.25, how many pieces are the two candy bars divided into? Use hundredths models to divide.

$2 \div 0.25 = n$

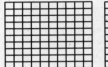

_____

3. The 4 relay team members ran a total of 2.4 miles. If each member ran the same amount of miles, how many miles did each relay member run?

_____

4. Michelle had $4.00. She bought candy bars that cost $0.40 each. How many candy bars did she buy?

_____

5. In the first race, the 4 member relay team ran a total of 3.2 miles. In the second race, they ran a total of 3.6 miles. If each member ran the same amount of miles, how many miles did each team member run?

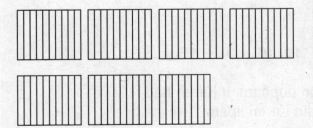

_____

6. Ellen has $2.00 in nickels and $3.00 in dimes. How many nickels and dimes does Ellen have?

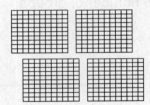

_____

Divide Decimals by Whole Numbers

CA Standards
KEY NS 2.1, **KEY** NS 2.2

Divide $2.70 \div 9 = n$
You can divide and place the decimal point in the quotient.

Step 1 Divide as you do with whole numbers. Ignore the decimal point.

$$\begin{array}{r} 30 \\ 9\overline{)2.70} \\ -270 \\ \hline 0 \end{array}$$

Step 2 Put a decimal point in the quotient directly above the decimal point in the dividend.

$$\begin{array}{r} 0.30 \\ 9\overline{)2.70} \\ -270 \\ \hline 0 \end{array}$$

Step 3 Multiply to check your work.

$$\begin{array}{r} 0.3 \\ \times\ 9 \\ \hline 2.7 \end{array}$$

Solution: $2.70 \div 9 = 0.30$

Find each quotient. Multiply to check your answer.

1. $9\overline{)8.1}$

2. $5\overline{)5.75}$

3. $7\overline{)18.2}$

4. $6\overline{)0.012}$

5. $2.4 \div 3 =$

6. $0.56 \div 8 =$

7. $21.06 \div 9 =$

8. $7.5 \div 5 =$

_____   _____   _____   _____

9. $4\overline{)25.92}$

10. $2\overline{)6.32}$

11. $7\overline{)3.22}$

12. $8\overline{)1.68}$

Spiral Review   (Chapter 5, Lesson 2) NS 1.3

Simplify.

13. $(8 + 14) - 12$ _____

14. $15 - (4 + 7)$ _____

15. Myra went to the pet store with her new puppy. She bought a toy for $5 and a bone for $3. She used a $10 bill to pay for the items. How much money did she receive as change?

_____

Divide Decimals by Whole Numbers

Solve Problems 1–6.

1. Four friends divided 1.2 of a batch of cookies. How many cookies did each friend receive? Use fractions to divide. Simplify.

$1.2 \div 4 = n$

Use models to check your work.

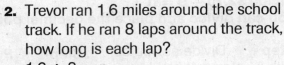

2. Trevor ran 1.6 miles around the school track. If he ran 8 laps around the track, how long is each lap?

$1.6 \div 8 = n$

Use models to solve.

_____

_____

3. Brian roller-skated around the playground 6 times. If he roller skated a total of 1.80 miles, what is the distance of one lap around the playground?

_____

4. Carl drove 3.28 miles on the go cart track. If Carl went around the track 4 times, how many kilometers was each lap?

_____

5. Five players on an ice hockey team skated a total of 6.3 kilometers on Saturday and 4.2 kilometers on Sunday. If they each skated an equal distance, how many kilometers did they each skate?

_____

6. A triathlon is broken into swimming, biking, and running races. Each race is the same distance. The total distance of the triathlon is 36.35 miles. How many miles are the swimming and biking races combined?

_____

Divide Whole Numbers with Decimal Quotients

CA Standards
KEY NS 2.1, **KEY** NS 2.2

Divide 8 ÷ 5.

Step 1 Write a decimal point in the dividend and a zero in the tenths place of the dividend.

$5\overline{)8.0}$

Step 2 Divide.

$$\begin{array}{r} 1.6 \\ 5\overline{)8.0} \\ -50 \\ \hline 30 \\ -30 \\ \hline 0 \end{array}$$

Step 3 To write the answer without a remainder, you can add zeros in the dividend and continue dividing.

Step 4 Multiply to check your answer.

Solution:
$5 \times 1.6 = 8$

Write each quotient as a decimal number. Multiply to check.

1. $3 \div 4 =$ _____

2. $5 \div 4 =$ _____

3. $6 \div 4 =$ _____

4. $2\overline{)7}$

5. $8\overline{)1}$

6. $6\overline{)3}$

Write each fraction as a decimal.

7. $\dfrac{6}{5}$ _____

8. $\dfrac{12}{15}$ _____

9. $\dfrac{9}{6}$ _____

Spiral Review (Chapter 7, Lesson 4) **KEY** NS 2.3

Add or subtract. Write your answer in simplest form.

10. $\dfrac{1}{4} + \dfrac{2}{8}$ _____

11. $\dfrac{7}{10} - \dfrac{2}{5}$ _____

12. A recipe called for $\dfrac{1}{2}$ cup of flour and $\dfrac{3}{4}$ cup of sugar. How much more sugar was added than flour?

_____

Use with text pp. 298–299

Name _____ Date _____

Divide Whole Numbers with Decimal Quotients

Solve.

1. Write the division expression as a fraction.

$2 \div 6 = n$

_____

2. Write the fraction as a division expression.

$\frac{3}{2} = n$

_____

3. Ethan divided 2 pounds of apples into 5 baskets. How many pounds of apples were in each basket?

_____

4. Pete spent $6.00 on 4 bags of oranges. How much did each bag cost?

_____

5. Gavin's Greens sold 4 cucumbers for $5.00. They sold 6 melons for $5.00. How much more did a melon cost than a cucumber?

_____

6. Frank's Farm sold a total of $10.00 of vegetables and $8.00 of fruit. They sold 15 pounds of produce. If all produce costs the same, how much does their produce cost per pound?

_____

Name _____ Date _____

Divide a Whole Number by a Decimal

CA Standards
KEY NS 2.1, KEY NS 2.2

Divide 14 ÷ 0.07. Divide by Hundredths.

Step ① Multiply the divisor and dividend by 100.

$$\times 100$$
$$\frac{14.0}{0.07} = \frac{1400}{7}$$
$$\times 100$$

Step ② Show it by moving both decimal points two places to the right.

$$7.\overline{)1400.}$$

Step ③ Place the decimal point in the quotient directly above the new decimal point in the dividend. Then divide.

Solution: 14 ÷ 0.07 = 200

Divide and check.

1. $17 \div 0.4 =$ _____

2. $16 \div 0.03 =$ _____

3. $1 \div 0.02 =$ _____

4. $33 \div 0.8 =$ _____

5. $45 \div 0.06 =$ _____

6. $9 \div 0.2 =$ _____

7. $19 \div 0.7 =$ _____

8. $4 \div 0.02 =$ _____

Spiral Review (Chapter 11, Lesson 2) **NS 2.4, NS 2.5**

Divide. Show your work.

9. $\frac{1}{4} \div 3 =$ _____

10. $\frac{2}{5} \div 4 =$ _____

11. $\frac{1}{8}$ of a pizza was left. Trevor and his brother divided the last slice into 2 pieces. What portion of the pizza was each slice?

_____

Use with text pp. 300–303

Divide a Whole Number by a Decimal

Solve.

1. A horse galloped 5 miles around the track. If each lap was 0.5 miles, how many laps did the horse make?

$$5 \div 0.5 = n$$

_____

2. Tyson picked up a crate of peppers that weighed 8 pounds. If each pepper weighed 0.4 pounds, how many peppers were in the crate?

$$8 \div 0.4 = n$$

_____

3. Mary is training for a 10-kilometer race. She runs 47 kilometers each week. If she runs 9.4 kilometers each day, how many days does she run each week?

_____

4. Kathy runs 63 kilometers per week. If she runs 10.5 kilometers each day, how many days does she run each week?

_____

5. The Smighen family is traveling by car on vacation. If they travel 540 miles in 2.4 days, and they drive the same distance each day, how many miles do they drive in a day?

_____

6. To reach the hiking trails, Darren drives 75 miles. His truck gets 13.6 miles per gallon. Rounded to the nearest tenth of a gallon, how many gallons does Darren use?

_____

Divide a Decimal by a Decimal

Find $12.5 \div 0.5$.
Move decimal points, divide, and place a decimal point in the quotient.

Step 1 Multiply the divisor and dividend by the same power of 10.

$$\overset{\times 10}{\underset{\times 10}{\frac{12.5}{0.5}}} = \frac{125}{5}$$

Step 2 Write a decimal point in the quotient directly above the new decimal point in the dividend. Then divide.

$$0.5\overline{)12.5} = 5\overline{)125.}$$

Step 3 If needed, write zeros after the decimal point in the dividend to continue dividing.

$$\frac{25}{5\overline{)125}} = 0.5\overline{)12.5}$$

Solution: $12.5 \div 0.5 = 25$

Divide. Estimate to check that your answer is reasonable.

1. $15.5 \div 0.2 =$

_____

2. $4.2 \div 0.6 =$

_____

3. $5.8 \div 0.4 =$

_____

4. $3.2 \div 0.2 =$

_____

5. $5.5 \div 0.5 =$

_____

6. $16.2 \div 0.8 =$

_____

7. $1.4 \div 0.2 =$

_____

8. $12.4 \div 0.4 =$

_____

Spiral Review   (Chapter 13, Lesson 2) **KEY** NS 2.1

Find the product.

9. 2.5×16 _____

10. 50×1.25 _____

11. Ms. Wright spent $1.65 on coffee each day for 5 days last week. How much did she spend altogether

_____

Name _____ Date _____

Divide a Decimal by a Decimal

Solve.

1. A pitcher held 6.4 ounces of water. The water was poured into ice-cube trays. Each ice cube held 0.4 ounces of water. How many ice cubes were made?

   $6.4 \div 0.4 = n$

   _____

2. Rose picked 3.5 pounds of tomatoes. If each tomato weighed 0.5 pound, how many tomatoes did she pick?

   $3.5 \div 0.5 = n$

   _____

3. Each lap of a running track is 0.5 kilometer. How many laps will a runner need to run in order to run 3.2 kilometers?

   _____

4. Derek plans to hike 17.2 miles in January. If he hikes 0.9 mile each time he hikes, how many times does he plan to hike in January?

   _____

5. Each lap of the Round Robin track is 0.6 mile. Each lap of the Twist 'n Turn track is 0.8 mile. If Will raced 2.75 miles around each track, how many laps did he make on each track? Round your answers to the nearest tenth.

   _____

   _____

   _____

6. Olivia had a jar of quarters that held a total of $14.50. Her sister's jar held $12.75 in quarters. How many more quarters does Olivia have?

   _____

   _____

   _____

   _____

   _____

   _____

Name _____ Date _____

Problem Solving:
Use a Simpler Problem

Adam wants to ride 375 miles in one month. If he uses a 6.25 mile bike path, how many times will he have to ride the path to reach his goal?

You can use simpler numbers to help you decide how to solve the problem.

Step 1 Choose simpler numbers to decide how to solve the problem. What if Adam wanted to bike 10 miles and the bike path was 0.5 miles long?

Divide. $10 \div 0.5 = 20$

Step 2 Reread the problem. Solve using the original numbers.

Divide. $375 \div 6.25 = 60$

So, Adam will have to ride the bike path 60 times.

Solve. Use a simpler problem. Explain why your answer makes sense.

1. The City Center Auditorium was renovated to have more seats. Now it has 2,160 seats, which is $1\frac{1}{8}$ times as many as it had before. How many seats did the auditorium have before renovation?

_____

_____

2. Tim used a pedometer to keep track of how many steps he took going up and down stairs in a week. In the first week, he took 576 steps. In the second week, he took $1\frac{3}{4}$ times as many. How many steps did he take in the second week?

_____

_____

Spiral Review (Chapter 13, Lesson 2) **KEY NS 2.1**

Find the product.

3. $3.7 \times 23 =$ _____

4. $78 \times 0.61 =$ _____

5. Joseph spends $2.70 each day at the school cafeteria. How much does Joseph spend in 20 days at the cafeteria?

_____

Name _____ Date _____

Problem Solving: Use a Simpler Problem

CA Standards
KEY NS 2.2, MR 2.2

Solve.

1. The grocery store is 30 miles from Anthony's house. The toy store is $1\frac{1}{5}$ times farther. How far is the toy store from Anthony's house?

2. Each week, the Walker family has a family movie night. Last week, they watched a 98-minute movie. This week, the movie they watched was $1\frac{1}{2}$ times longer. How long was this week's movie?

3. At a party, Tara's friends ate 60 cookies. Garth's friends ate 1.75 more cookies than Tara's friends. How many cookies did Garth's friends eat?

4. Lucy's hair is $1\frac{1}{4}$ times longer than Jenna's hair. If Lucy's hair is 30 centimeters long, how long is Jenna's hair?

5. Tim has a 64 MB memory card and a 32 MB memory card for his digital camera. The 64 MB card is 68% full, and the 32 MB card is 44% full. Which card has more empty memory, and by how many MB?

6. Drew has $756 in his checking account. Drew has 1.09 times less than Taylor and $1\frac{1}{4}$ times more than Joe. How much money do Taylor and Joe have in their checking accounts?

132

Hands On: Divide with Multiples of 10, 100 and 1,000

Look for patterns when dividing by multiples of 10, 100, and 1,000.

Find $36,000 \div 4$	Find $335,000 \div 1,000$	Estimate $18,000 \div 500$
$36 \div 4 = 9$	$335,000 \div 1 = 335,000$	$18,000 \div 500$
$360 \div 4 = 90$	$335,000 \div 10 = 33,500$	$15 \div 5 = 3$
$3,600 \div 4 = 900$	$335,000 \div 100 = 3,350$	$15,000 \div 500 = 30$
$36,000 \div 4 = 9,000$	$335,000 \div 1,000 = 335$	$20 \div 5 = 4$
		$20,000 \div 500 = 40$

The quotient is between 30 and 40.

Use mental math to find each quotient.

1. $810 \div 9 =$

2. $480 \div 60 =$

3. $6,300 \div 900 =$

4. $4,500 \div 500 =$

_____ _____ _____ _____

5. $56,000 \div 700 =$

6. $40,000 \div 8,000 =$

7. $210,000 \div 3,000 =$

8. $540,000 \div 9,000 =$

_____ _____ _____ _____

9. $800\overline{)24,000}$

10. $3,000\overline{)180,000}$

11. $600\overline{)300,000}$

12. $9,000\overline{)360,000}$

Spiral Review (Chapter 6, Lesson 2) AF 1.3

Use the Distributive Property to find the value of the variable.

13. $5 \times 82 = (5 \times n) + (5 \times 2): n =$ _____

14. $3 \times 52 = (3 \times n) + (3 \times 2): n =$ _____

15. There are 3 fifth grade classes at Webbville Elementary. Each class has 32 students. How many fifth grade students attend Webbville Elementary?

_____

Hands On: Divide with Multiples of 10, 100 and 1,000

Use basic facts and patterns to find quotients. Show your work.

1. Fifty schools sent 400 students to a mathematics competition. If each school sent the same number of students, how many students did each school send?

   $40 \div 5 =$

   $400 \div 50 =$

2. There are 2,100 students at Spring Green Middle School. If the school has 70 classes, and each class has the same number of students, how many students are in each class?

   $21 \div 7 =$

   $2,100 \div 70 =$

3. Maryville Middle School spent $16,000 to purchase computers. If the school bought 40 computers, and each computer cost the same amount, what was the cost of each computer?

4. The Parent Teacher Association bought new whiteboards for the school. The total amount spent was $24,000 for 10 whiteboards. How much did one whiteboard cost?

5. Lake View High School performed a musical play for 3 consecutive nights in May. The revenue for each performance was $18,000. If each ticket was $30, how many total tickets were sold?

6. A Board of Education allocated $640,000 to renovate the schools in a district. If each school receives $80,000, how many schools are in the district?

Estimate Quotients

CA Standards
KEY NS 2.2, MR 2.2

Step ① Estimate 1,632 ÷ 24	Step ② Use multiples of ten to find a new dividend and divisor.	Step ③ Divide using the new dividend and divisor.
Think: Which basic fact will help solve the problem? $16 \div 2 = 8$ **Solution:** 80	$1632 \div 24$ ↓ ↓ $1600 \div 20$	$1600 \div 20 = 80$

Use compatible numbers to estimate each quotient.

1. 177 ÷ 36

☐ ÷ ☐ = ☐

2. 915 ÷ 89

☐ ÷ ☐ = ☐

3. 1,962 ÷ 59

☐ ÷ ☐ = ☐

4. 1,241 ÷ 62 =

_____

5. 5,140 ÷ 75 =

_____

6. 38,425 ÷ 610 =

_____

7. 1,156 ÷ 62 =

_____

8. 26,934 ÷ 25 =

_____

9. 65,425 ÷ 810 =

_____

Spiral Review (Chapter 6, Lesson 2) **AF 1.3**

Use the Distributive Property to find the value of the variable.

10. $a \times 93 = (5 \times 90) + (5 \times 3)$ _____

11. $8 \times c = (8 \times 60) + (8 \times 7)$ _____

12. Rob used the Distributive Property to solve a multiplication problem. Look at Rob's work. What is Rob's error? Correct the error and explain your thinking.

$6 \times 143 = (6 \times 14) + (6 \times 3)$

_____

_____

_____

Name _____ Date _____

Estimate Quotients

CA Standards
KEY NS 2.2, MR 2.2

The Spring Green School District held a Family Fun Day to raise money for new technology supplies.

Use compatible numbers to estimate each quotient. Show your work.

1. A class set of 25 calculators cost $285. About how much is each calculator?

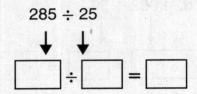

$285 \div 25$

2. The school district ordered 315 balloons for math night. The balloons were packaged in bags of 45. About how many bags were ordered?

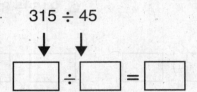

$315 \div 45$

3. One thousand souvenirs were ordered to give away as prizes. If the souvenirs were packed in boxes of 25, about how many boxes were ordered?

4. The plant booth sold 290 plants to 76 customers. If each customer bought the same amount of plants, about how many did each customer purchase?

5. During the event, there were 28 musicians that performed. The program continued through the night for a total of 5 hours. About how many minutes did each musician have to perform?

6. The pizza stand sold 679 pieces of pizza for a total of $1,316. Of the pieces sold, 425 were pepperoni and 254 were cheese. Estimate the cost of each piece of pizza.

Divide by 2-Digit Divisors

Divide 648 ÷ 12.

Step 1 Estimate.

$648 \div 12 =$

$600 \div 10 = 60$

Step 2 Divide.

```
      54
12)648
    -60
     48
    -48
      0
```

Step 3 Check by multiplying the divisor by the quotient.

```
   54
  ×12
  108
 +540
  648
```

Solution: $648 \div 12 = 54$

Divide. Check your answer.

1. $18)\overline{54}$

2. $31)\overline{372}$

3. $2.2)\overline{33}$

4. $16)\overline{97.6}$

_____ _____ _____ _____

5. $3.4)\overline{81.6}$

6. $55)\overline{330}$

7. $27)\overline{83.7}$

8. $4.5)\overline{94.5}$

_____ _____ _____ _____

9. $54.4 \div 17 =$

10. $23.2 \div 58 =$

11. $72.3 \div 7.5 =$

12. $34.8 \div 2.9 =$

_____ _____ _____ _____

Spiral Review (Chapter 10, Lessons 2 and 3) **NS 2.4, NS 2.5**

Solve. Write your answer in simplest form.

13. $\frac{1}{4} \times \frac{1}{7} =$ _____

14. $\frac{5}{8} \times \frac{4}{5} =$ _____

15. Susie is using $2\frac{3}{4}$ cups of nuts for each batch of her cookie recipe. If she makes 3 batches of cookies, how many cups of nuts will Susie need?

_____

Divide by 2-Digit Divisors

Divide. Check your answers.

1. Cari's van traveled 435 miles at an average speed of 60 miles per hour. How many hours did Cari drive?

   $435 \div 60 =$

   _____

2. On another trip the car that runs on vegetable oil traveled 445.4 miles using 13.1 gallons of vegetable oil. What is the fuel efficiency in miles per gallon?

   $13.1 \overline{)445.4}$

   _____

3. A bus trip from Washington D.C. to Charleston, South Carolina, takes about 11 hours. If the distance of the trip is 797.5 miles, at what speed did the bus travel?

   _____

4. It takes about 11 hours to travel from Baltimore to Hawaii by air. Depending on the flight route, the jet may fly 6,600 miles. What is the speed of the jet in miles per hour?

   _____

5. It is approximately 9,500 miles to China. If a jumbo jet travels 19 hours, how fast is the jet traveling (in miles per hour)?

   _____

6. An electric hybrid car may travel as far as 1,300 miles on a tank of gasoline. If the tank holds 12.5 gallons of gasoline, how may miles will the car travel on one gallon of gasoline?

   _____

Estimated Quotient Is Too Large or Too Small

CA Standards
KEY NS 2.2, **KEY** NS 2.1

A sports utility vehicle can travel 21 miles on one gallon of gasoline.
How many gallons would be needed to travel 525 miles?

Step ① Estimate and divide.

$525 \div 21$

$$\begin{array}{r} 3 \\ 21\overline{)525} \\ 63 \end{array}$$

Think: $63 > 52$, so the estimate is too high.

Step ② Adjust and divide.

$$\begin{array}{r} 25 \\ 21\overline{)525} \\ -42 \downarrow \\ \hline 105 \\ -105 \\ \hline 0 \end{array}$$

Solution: A sports utility vehicle would need 25 gallons of gasoline to travel 525 miles.

Divide.

1. $6.4 \div 0.8 =$ _____

2. $14.4 \div 0.6 =$ _____

3. $32.07 \div 0.1 =$ _____

4. $1.9\overline{)38}$

5. $6.5\overline{)15.6}$

6. $12\overline{)288}$

Spiral Review (Chapter 12, Lesson 3) **KEY** NS 2.1

Add or subtract.

7. $3.58 - 0.679 =$ _____

8. $1.24 + 0.862 + 15.9 =$ _____

9. At a car race, JJ Johnson's final time was 28.802 seconds.
Bobby Lane's time for the same race was 29.015 seconds.
What is the difference in their times? How do you know who
was the winner of the race?

_____

_____

Name _____ Date _____

Estimated Quotient Is Too Large or Too Small

Batting averages are used to determine how well a player performs at bat. To find a batting average, divide the number of hits by the number of times at bat.

Divide to determine batting averages.

1. Dugout Dan has 14 hits and 50 times at bat. What is his batting average?

   $14 \div 50 =$

   _____

2. Pop-up Paul has 24 hits and 96 times at bat. What is his batting average?

   _____

3. Homerun Henry has 75 hits and 150 times at bat. Estimate his batting average and explain your reasoning.

   _____

   _____

   _____

4. Fastball Fran has had 100 times at bat and 31 hits. Estimate her batting average, then find the actual batting average.

   _____

   _____

   _____

   _____

   _____

5. If Line-drive Lewis hits 72 times out of 250 times at bat, and DJ Dividem hits 35 times out of 125 times at bat, what is the difference between their batting averages?

   _____

6. Sally Singleton's batting average is 0.375 and she has been at bat 120 times. How may times has Sally hit the ball?

   _____

4- and 5-Digit Dividends

CA Standards
KEY NS 2.2, KEY NS 2.1

Eighteen pioneers pack 2,448 pounds of food for traveling on the Oregon Trail. How many pounds of food were packed for each person?

Step 1 Estimate.

$$\begin{array}{r} 100 \\ 20\overline{)2000} \end{array}$$

Think: $20 \times 100 = 2,000$. So, 100 pounds is too small for the number of pounds per person.

Step 2 Divide.

$$\begin{array}{r} 136 \\ 18\overline{)2,448} \\ \underline{18} \\ 64 \\ \underline{54} \\ 108 \\ \underline{108} \\ 0 \end{array}$$

Step 3 Check

$$\begin{array}{r} 136 \\ \times\ 18 \\ \hline 1088 \\ 1360 \\ \hline 2,448 \end{array}$$

Solution: There were 136 pounds of food for each person.

Divide. Check your work.

1. $42\overline{)1,764}$

2. $57\overline{)2,280}$

3. $91\overline{)7,189}$

4. $7.9\overline{)48.19}$

5. $0.31\overline{)189.1}$

6. $6.5\overline{)64.155}$

Spiral Review (Chapter 14, Lessons 2, 3 and 4) **KEY** NS 2.2, **KEY** NS 2.1

Divide.

7. $9\overline{)8.1}$

8. $0.7\overline{)49}$

9. The settlers packed 24.4 pounds of coffee for 4 people. How many pounds of coffee could each person use to make coffee?

_____

Name _____ Date _____

4- and 5-Digit Dividends

CA Standards
KEY NS 2.2, **KEY** NS 2.1

Divide. Check your answers.

1. Pioneers saw 2,394 buffalo as they traveled the Oregon Trail. If the buffalo were in herds of 38, how many buffalo herds did the pioneers see?

$$\begin{array}{r} 6 \\ 38\overline{)2{,}394} \end{array}$$

_____

2. A wagon train stopped for rest over night. Together, the 28 families had over 13,972 pounds of supplies. If each family had the same amount of supplies, how many pounds did each family have?

$$\begin{array}{r} 4 \\ 28\overline{)13{,}972} \end{array}$$

_____

3. A pioneer family settled in Oregon and bought sixty-eight acres for $79.56. How much did the family pay per acre?

_____

4. If you travel to California, you can still pan for gold like the settlers did over 100 years ago. One settler found $345.87 worth of gold. If the cost of the gold was $6.10 per gram, how many grams of gold did he find?

_____

5. If an estimated 167,925 settlers headed out West between 1840 and 1865, how many people traveled West each year?

_____

6. During the gold rush, California's population grew dramatically. Suppose 312,876 people moved to California between January 1855 and June 1859. How many people moved to California each month?

_____

Problem Solving: Use the Remainder

Example 1
Joe has 67 ounces of water to pour into 8-ounce containers. How many containers will he use?

$67 \div 8 = 8 \text{ R}3$

Joe will fill 8 containers and use 1 more for the remaining 3 ounces.

Solution: Joe will use 9 containers.

Example 2
Mr. Evans spent $255 on 20 new textbooks for his class. What was the price of each textbook?

$\$255 \div 20 = \$12.75$

Solution: The price of each textbook was $12.75

Solve. Explain how you used the remainder.

1. Jake has 123 books to put on shelves. Each shelf will hold 14 books. How many shelves will he use?

_____

_____

2. Sarah spent $10.00 to rent 8 movies. What was the price of each movie?

_____

_____

Spiral Review (Chapter 14, Lessons 2, 3 and 4) **KEY NS 2.2, KEY NS 2.1**

Divide.

3. $7\overline{)6.3}$ _____

4. $0.5\overline{)75}$ _____

5. Julia spent $42.80 at a coffee shop with friends. If she bought coffee for herself and 9 friends, how much did each cup of coffee cost?

_____

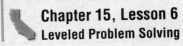

Name _____ Date _____

Problem Solving: Use the Remainder

CA Standards
KEY NS 2.2, MR 2.6

Solve. Explain how you used the remainder.

1. Mrs. Jones has her students share copies of worksheets in class. There are 19 students in the class. If she has 3 students share one copy, how many copies should Mrs. Jones make? Hint: Divide 19 by 3. If there is a remainder, those students will need a copy too.

   _____

   _____

2. Parker spends 9 hours per week on his homework. He has 5 subjects and wants to divide the time he spends on homework evenly among the subjects. How long will he spend on each subject? Divide 9 by 5 to find the answer.

   _____

   _____

3. Last year, Karla spent a total of $140 to get her car washed 16 times. How much did she pay each time?

   _____

   _____

4. Mr. Baxter has a roll of 52 feet of paper for his art class. There are 16 students in the class, and Mr. Baxter plans to divide the paper equally among the students. How much paper will each student get?

   _____

   _____

5. Gayle manages a hotel and needs new appliances for the guest rooms. She plans to spend $715 on 6 refrigerators and 8 microwaves. If the refrigerators cost $71.50 each, what is the price of each microwave?

   _____

   _____

6. The Calvin family uses one cable provider for cable TV, internet, and digital phone services. They pay $138 a month for the combination of services. If they paid for each service separately, they would pay $60 for cable TV, $35 for internet, and $55 for digital phone. What is their daily savings for a 30-day month?

   _____

   _____

Hands On: Model Finding the Mean

CA Standard
SDAP 1.1

Find the mean of this set of numbers. Use counters.

6, 7, 8, 5, 6, 4

Step 1 Make a column of counters for each number in the list.

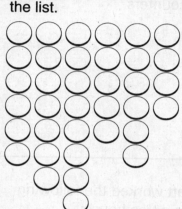

Step 2 Rearrange the columns of counters so that each one has the same number.

Step 3 Determine the number of counters in each even column.

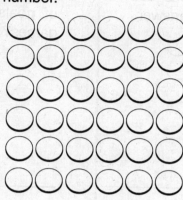

There are 6 counters in each column, so the mean of this set of numbers is 6.

Find the mean of each set of numbers. Use counters.

1. 5, 6, 9, 8, 9, 5 _____

2. 2, 4, 5, 3, 5, 5 _____

3. 2, 3, 5, 5, 1, 2 _____

4. 3, 6, 8, 7, 9, 3 _____

Spiral Review (Chapter 9, Lesson 4) **KEY NS 2.3, NS 2.0**

Subtract. Then simplify your answer.

5. $3\frac{3}{4} - 1\frac{1}{4}$ _____

6. $6\frac{2}{3} - 1\frac{5}{6}$ _____

7. Bryan and Kathryn were making a mural for their classroom by coloring tiles. In one hour, Bryan colored $8\frac{1}{5}$ tiles. Kathryn colored $6\frac{2}{3}$ tiles in the same time. How much more did Bryan color than Kathryn?

Hands On: Model Finding the Mean

CA Standard
SDAP 1.1

Solve.

1. To find the mean, Susan has to move counters below until all the columns have the same number. How many counters will be in each column? Use counters to help you find the answer.

_____

2. Ted played three games of soccer. He scored 2 goals in the first game, 1 goal in the second game, and 3 goals in the third game. What is the mean number of goals Ted scored during the three games? Use counters.

_____

3. This year for his birthday, Louis received 5 books. Last year he received 4 books. Two years ago he got 7 books, and three years ago he got 4 books. What is the mean number of books Louis received each birthday for the last four years?

_____

4. Sarah and Matt worked the following hours building a tree house:

Week 1: 8   **Week 2:** 9

Week 3: 5   **Week 4:** 6

What is the mean number of hours they worked per week?

_____

5. Marc asked his classmates to keep track of how long they rode the bus each week. The results are shown below. What is the mean number of hours that Marc's classmates spend on the bus each week?

3, 5, 3, 6, 4, 3, 6, 2, 5, 1, 3, 4, 5, 6, 5, 2, 5

_____

6. At Frederick's school, $\frac{1}{3}$ of the teachers give homework 4 times a week, $\frac{7}{15}$ give homework 3 times a week, and $\frac{1}{5}$ give homework twice a week. What is the average number of times a teacher gives homework at Frederick's school? Round your answer to the nearest whole number.
Hint: Find a possible total number of teachers first.

_____

Mean, Median, and Mode

CA Standards
SDAP 1.1, SDAP 1.2

Find the mean, median, and mode for this set of data.

> 15, 40, 30, 20, 15, 40, 15
>
> **Step 1** Find the mean. Add the numbers. Divide the sum by the number of addends.
>
> $15 + 40 + 30 + 20 + 15 + 40 + 15 = 175$
>
> $175 \div 7 = 25$
>
> **Step 2** Find the median. Write the data in order from least to greatest. There are 7 numbers, so the median is the fourth number from either end.
>
> 15, 15, 15, ⬚20⬚, 30, 40, 40
>
> **Step 3** Find the mode. Underline the numbers that occur more than once. The mode is the number that occurs most often.
>
> 15, 40, 30, 20, 15, 40, 15
>
> 15 occurs more times than 40.
>
> **Solution:** The mean is 25, the median is 20, and the mode is 15.

Use the data in the table to complete Problems 1–4.

> **Time in Seconds**
> 65, 57, 63, 60, 63, 65, 59, 61, 65

1. What is the mean of the time in seconds? _____

2. What is the order of this data set arranged from least to greatest? _____

3. What is the median of the time in seconds? _____

4. What is the mode of the time in seconds? _____

Spiral Review (Chapter 9, Lesson 4) **KEY NS 2.3, NS 2.0**

Subtract. Then simplify your answer.

5. $6\frac{3}{5} - 2\frac{1}{5}$ _____

6. $5\frac{1}{4} - 3\frac{1}{2}$ _____

7. For their violin recital, Ed and Laura each had to memorize 6 songs. By the end of the first week of practice, Laura had memorized $3\frac{1}{2}$ songs and Ed had memorized $1\frac{7}{8}$ songs. How much more had Laura memorized than Ed?

Mean, Median, and Mode

CA Standards
SDAP 1.1, SDAP 1.2

Solve.

1. Matt works on his family's farm six days a week. The table shows the number of hours he works in one week.

Matt's Work Hours
1, 2, 1, 1, 3, 4

What is the average amount of time that Matt works each day? HINT: Add to find the total number of hours. Then divide by the number of days that Matt works.

_____

2. Rhonda and her cousins ride their bikes on the weekends. The table shows the number of miles they rode last month. What is the mode for the number of miles that they rode each weekend? **Hint:** The mode is the number that appears most frequently.

Miles Biked
12, 8, 7, 10, 9, 7, 8, 8

3. Ms. Standish's class took a history quiz that was worth 40 points. The scores of one group of students was 29, 27, 20, 24, 35, 22, 20, 28, and 20. What was the mean score for the group?

_____

4. What are the median and mode for the scores in Problem 3?

_____

5. Mr. Montgomery swims every day. The table shows the number of minutes he swam each day for the last 10 days.

Minutes Swimming
41, 50, 57, 60, 45,
41, 22, 41, 43, 44

Find the mean, median, and mode for this set of data. You may use decimals in your answers.

_____

_____

6. Karly's family took a cross-country sightseeing trip. For the first 9 days, they drove the following number of miles each day: 235, 168, 232, 193, 216, 138, 246, 91, 118. What is the mean number of miles they drove per day? The median? The mode? Round each number to the nearest whole mile.

_____

_____

Make Line Graphs

CA Standard
KEY SDAP 1.4

Chris kept track of how many ounces of water he drank each day for one week.

Ounces of Water Chris Drank					
Day	Mon.	Tues.	Wed.	Thurs.	Fri.
Ounces	56	52	60	45	54

Solution:

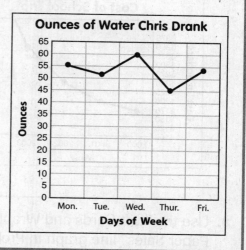

Step 1 Draw the axes. Label the horizontal axis Day and the vertical axis Ounces. Choose an appropriate scale and mark equal intervals.

Step 2 Plot the ordered pairs and join the points to make the line graph.

Step 3 Give the graph a title.

1. Use the data table of Mike's Miles Hiked to make a line graph.

Mike's Miles Hiked						
Day	1	2	3	4	5	6
Miles	5	10	16	22	27	31

2. Use your Mike's Miles Hiked line graph from Problem 1 and the Ben's Miles Hiked data to make a double line graph.

Ben's Miles Hiked						
Day	1	2	3	4	5	6
Miles	0	4	10	15	21	25

Spiral Review (Chapter 11, Lessons 1–3) **NS 2.4, NS 2.5**

Write each quotient in simplest form.

3. $5 \div \frac{3}{4}$

_____

4. $\frac{8}{9} \div \frac{4}{5}$

_____

5. Beth and Cameron have $4\frac{5}{8}$ cookies and each want an equal share. If they divide the cookies equally between the two of them, how much will each person get?

_____

Make Line Graphs

CA Standard
KEY SDAP 1.4

Solve.

1. How much did the school trip cost in 2002?

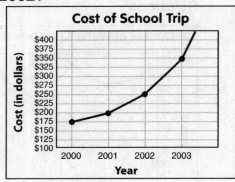

2. Use the "Cost of School Trip" line graph from Problem 1. How much did the cost of the trip increase from 2000 to 2002?

3. Use the "Gift Cards and Wrapping Paper Sales" line graph in Problem 4. How much did the class raise from September to January by selling gift cards? How much did they raise from selling wrapping paper?

4. In which month was there the greatest difference between gift card sales and wrapping paper sales?

5. The table shows the number of pennies Oscar collected. Make a line graph of the data.

Pennies Collected by Oscar

Day	1	2	3	4	5
Pennies	150	225	300	210	175

6. Use your "Pennies Collected by Oscar" line graph from Problem 5 and Britt's data to make a double line graph.

Pennies Collected by Brit

Day	1	2	3	4	5
Pennies	200	110	320	165	260

Circle Graphs

CA Standard
AF 1.1, SDAP 1.2

100 students took a survey. Look at the circle graph of the results. Which flavor received the most votes? How many students chose this flavor?

Step ❶ The largest section of the circle graph is chocolate.

Step ❷ Chocolate was chosen by 45% of the students. $100 \times 0.45 = 45$

Solution: Chocolate was the flavor that received the most votes. There were 45 students who chose this flavor.

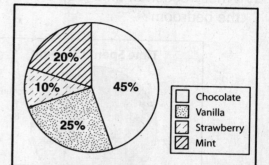

Use the circle graph to answer Problems 1–3.

Nick and Cassie made fruit salad for the family picnic. The circle graph shows what fruit made up each fraction of the fruit salad.

1. What fraction of the fruit salad was made up of strawberries? _____

2. What fraction of the fruit salad was made up of melons and apples? _____

3. If the entire salad weighed 32 ounces, how much did the bananas weigh? _____

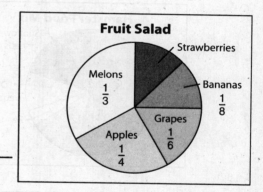

Spiral Review (Chapter 13, Lesson 3) **NS 1.1, KEY NS 2.1**

Estimate each product. Write an equation to show the rounded numbers you used.

4. 6.327×9.814

5. 15×1.65

6. After 15 minutes, Mr. Sidney has cleaned 4.92 chalk boards. If he continues for the entire hour at the same rate, approximately how many boards will he have cleaned?

_____

Name _____ Date _____

Circle Graphs

CA Standard
AF 1.1, SDAP 1.2

Solve.

1. What fraction of time is spent cleaning the bedroom?

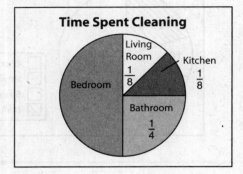

2. Use the circle graph on time spent cleaning in Problem 1. Pam spent a total of 2 hours cleaning the house. How many minutes did she spend cleaning the bathroom?

_____

3. If a bag of food weighs 32 ounces, what weight is made up of corn?

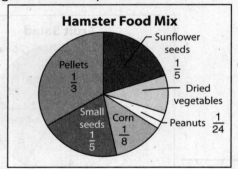

4. Use the circle graph about hamster food mix in Problem 3. Which ingredients in the hamster food mix are used in equal amounts?

_____

5. Arrange the toys in order from greatest fraction to least fraction.

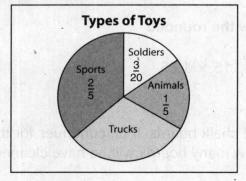

6. Valerie's band rehearses two days a week for $1\frac{1}{2}$ hours each day. A circle graph shows that $\frac{1}{6}$ of each rehearsal is spent marching, and $\frac{1}{8}$ of each rehearsal is spent taking attendance and passing out music. If the rest of the time is spent playing music, what fraction of the graph should be labeled Playing Music? How many minutes per week does that fraction represent?

Name _____ Date _____

Histograms

CA Standards
SDAP 1.2, AF 1.1

The data below show the scores of one fifth-grade class on a science test.
Were there more scores from 61–70, 71–80, 81–90, or 91–100?

90	67	78	71	97	85	89	76	99	100	68
75	88	68	85	84	95	78	82	86	92	80

Make a Frequency Table

Step 1 Look at the data to decide what intervals to use. This question includes four equal intervals.

Step 2 Make one tally mark for each score.

Step 3 Count the tally marks and write the frequencies.

Make a Histogram

Step 1 Draw the axes. Label the vertical axis. Choose an equally spaced scale.

Step 2 Label the horizontal axis and list the four score ranges.

Step 3 Draw a bar for each score range. Do not leave spaces between the bars. Give the graph a title.

1. Make a Frequency Table using the data above.

2. Make a Histogram using the data above.

Science Test Scores		
Score	**Tally**	**Number**
61–70		
71–80		
81–90		
91–100		

3. More students scored from _____ than in the other score ranges.

Spiral Review (Chapter 15, Lesson 2) **KEY NS 2.2**

Find the quotient. Check by multiplying.

4. $640 \div 10 =$ _____

5. $5,450 \div 100 =$ _____

6. Harrison was in charge of food for the school's open house dinner. He ordered 300 dinner rolls. If 100 people attend the dinner, how many rolls would each person get if the rolls were divided equally? _____

Name _____ Date _____

Histograms

Solve. Use the graph for problems 1–4.

1. In what age group were most of the presidents when they were inaugurated?

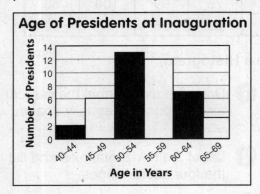

2. How many presidents were inaugurated when they were 60–64 years old?
Hint: The bar for this age group is between two numbers. What number is between 6 and 8?

3. How many more presidents were inaugurated in the 55–59 age group than in the 40–44 age group?

4. Suppose the next president inaugurated is 73 years old. Explain how this information would change the histogram.

5. This list shows average snowfall in inches for 20 cities in January.

| 10.4, 12, 2.4, 4.6, 7, 12.7, 5.7, 11.8, 10.5, 7.5, 10.3, 25.6, 8.7, 15.3, 7, 15, 10.8, 5.1, 12.3, 37.6 |

Make a frequency table and histogram to show the data.

6. Valdez, Alaska, gets an average of 66.3 inches of snow in January. How would this information change the frequency table and histogram you made in Problem 5?

Choose an Appropriate Graph

CA Standards
MR 2.3, SDAP 1.2

Use a graph to display the data set. Explain your choice of graph.

Line Graphs	Circle Graph	Histogram
When the data shows a change over time, a line graph is appropriate.	When the data shows parts of a whole, a circle graph is appropriate.	When the data is compared in equal intervals, a histogram is appropriate.
The track meet was held over a three day period.	There were 50 students in all who signed up for Field Day.	Students of different ages participated in the relay races.
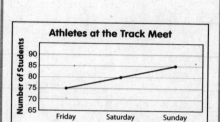	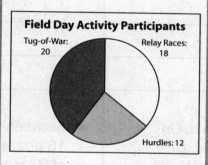	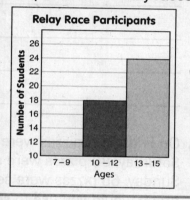

1. By the end of the relay race, 13 teams had finished between 5–7 minutes, 16 teams between 8–10 minutes, and 12 teams between 11–13 minutes.

_____

_____

_____

Spiral Review (Chapter 15, Lesson 2) **KEY NS 2.2**

Find the quotient. Check by multiplying.

2. 6,400 ÷ 100 _____

3. 2,450 ÷ 10 _____

4. There were 1,800 people at a football game. They were allowed into the stadium in 10 equal groups. How many people were in each group?

_____

Name _____ Date _____

Choose an Appropriate Graph

Solve. Use a graph to display the data set. Explain your choice of graph.

1. A histogram shows the amount of time different pizzas baked. There were 7 pizzas that baked for 10–12 minutes. Why is a histogram the most appropriate graph for this data?

_____

_____

_____

2. A circle graph shows the different pizza toppings that 70 customers chose. There were 25 customers who chose cheese, 30 who chose pepperoni, and 15 who chose sausage. Why is a circle graph the most appropriate graph for this data?

_____

_____

_____

3. On Friday, 75 pizzas were sold. On Saturday, 80 pizzas were sold. On Sunday, 65 pizzas were sold. Which graph would you use to show this data?

_____

_____

_____

4. Between the hours of 4 P.M. and 6 P.M., 15 pizzas were sold. Between the hours of 6 P.M. and 8 P.M., 35 pizzas were sold. Between the hours of 8 P.M. and 10 P.M., 25 pizzas were sold. Which graph would you use to show this data?

_____

_____

_____

5. Create a table that represents the data shown in the graph.

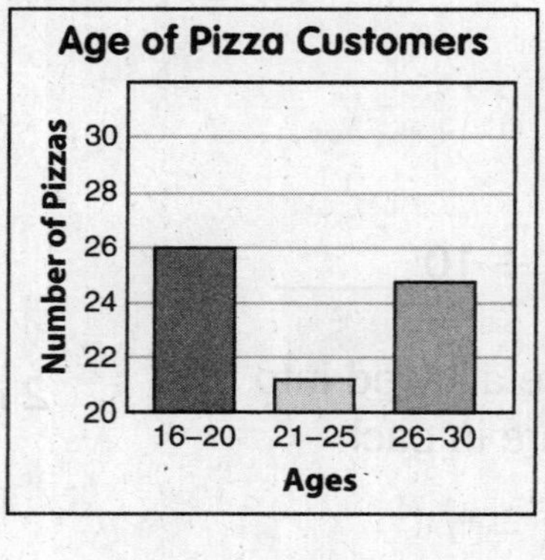

Age of Pizza Customers

6. What is another kind of graph you could draw to represent the data from problem 5? Draw the graph on a separate sheet of paper.

_____

_____

_____

Hands On: Plot points on a Coordinate Grid

CA Standards
KEY SDAP 1.4, **KEY** SDAP 1.5

Use the coordinate grid to plot point H at (5, 3).

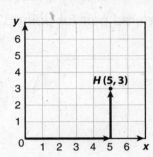

Step **1** Start at the origin (0, 0).

Step **2** From the origin, move five units to the right along the *x*-axis.

Step **3** From where you stopped in Step 2, move 3 units up along the *y*-axis.

Step **4** Mark and label the point with the ordered pair.

Use the coordinate grid to plot each point. Label each point with its letter. Connect the points in order to make a closed figure. Write the name of each figure.

1. A (4, 6) B (4, 4) C (6, 4) D (6, 6)

_____

2. E (3, 5) F (6, 0) G (3, 0)

_____

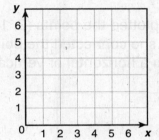

Spiral Review (Chapter 5, Lesson 5) **KEY** AF 1.5, AF 1.0

Copy and complete each function table.

3.

$y = 2x - 6$	
x	y
10	
12	18
14	

4.

$y = 14 - 3x$	
x	y
0	
1	
4	

5. The equation $y = 3x$ represents the amount of money Simone earns (*y*) if it takes her *x* hours to do her chores. Find how much money Simone makes if it takes her 2 hours to do her chores.

Name _____ Date _____

Hands On: Plot Points on a Coordinate Grid

Solve.

1. Justin plotted point T on the coordinate grid. Describe the movement Justin made to plot point T.

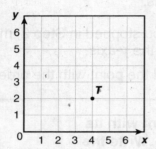

_____

2. What is the ordered pair for point B?

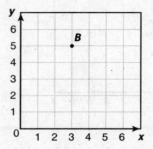

_____

3. Mrs. Harris plotted the points (2, 1) and (2, 5). After she connected the points, did she form a horizontal or vertical line?

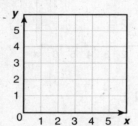

_____

4. Karen plotted point G below. She said the ordered pair for point G was (2, 3). Explain her mistake.

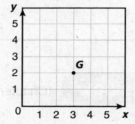

_____

_____

5. Marianne plotted the ordered pairs (4, 1), (1, 1), (4, 5). She connects these points and a fourth point to make a rectangle. What is the ordered pair for the missing point?

_____

6. The map of the school showed the location of the library, art room, music room, and gymnasium. The school office is located at the origin, (0, 0). The library is located at (2, 3), the art room at (2, 5), the music room at (4, 5), and the gymnasium at (6, 4). What is the distance between the art room and the music room?

_____

Interpret Graphs of Ordered Pairs

CA Standards
KEY SDAP 1.4, AF 1.1

How many miles did the soccer team run on Day 4?

Find the value of *y*, when *x* is 4.

**Step ① ** From the origin, move 4 units right along the *x*-axis "Day of Practice."

**Step ② ** Move up to the point marked on the graph.

**Step ③ ** Read the value on the *y*-axis, "Number of Miles Run." When *x* is 4, *y* is 5. The ordered pair is (4, 5).

Solution: The soccer team ran 5 miles on Day 4.

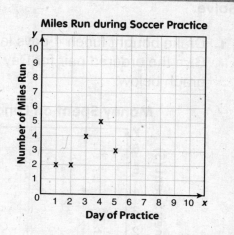

Miles Run during Soccer Practice

Use the graph of miles run during soccer practice to solve.

1. On which days did the team run the same distance? _____

2. Which day did the team run the greatest number of miles? _____

3. How many miles did the team run during the entire week? _____

Spiral Review (Chapter 5, Lesson 5) **KEY AF 1.5, AF 1.0**

Complete and copy each function table.

4.

y = x + 6	
x	**y**
3	9
	11

5.

y = 8 + 2x	
x	**y**
2	12
3	

6. Jeff is planting a garden. He plants 6 plants in each row. The total number of plants is given by the function y = 6x, where x is the number of rows. How many plants are there if the garden has 12 rows?

_____

Interpret Graphs of Ordered Pairs

CA Standards
KEY SDAP 1.4, AF 1.1

Solve.

1. Drake bought lunch 4 days last week. Give the ordered pair for Day 1 of the graph below.

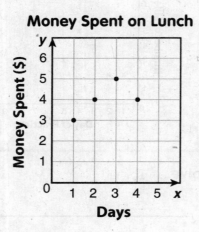

_____

2. Use the graph to tell how much money Drake spent on lunch on Day 2.

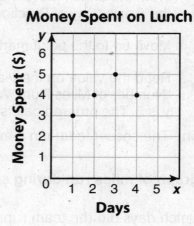

_____

3. Use the graph below to identify how many students brought in money on Day 2.

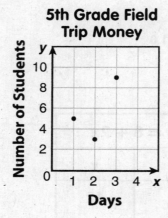

_____

4. Use the graph from problem 3 to find the total number of students who brought in their money after three days. Explain.

_____

_____

_____

_____

_____

5. The equation of a function is $y = 3x$. Give the value of y when $x = 6$. Give the ordered pair that would be plotted on a graph.

_____

6. Nate learned 5 new Spanish words every day in class. The equation of this function is $y = 5x$. Write the ordered pair for the tenth day.

_____

Graphs of Functions

CA Standards
KEY AF 1.5, **KEY** SDAP 1.5

Sara bought several $3 tubes of paint at the art supply store and used a coupon for $2 off. The total cost of Sara's order is a function of the number of tubes of paint she purchased. She can use the equation $y = 3x - 2$, where x is the number of tubes of paint, to represent the function.

Make a graph to show the possible total amounts of Sara's purchases.

Step ❶ Make a function table with x and y columns for the function.

Step ❷ Substitute each value of x into the function to find the value of y.

Step ❸ Use the function table to plot the points on the coordinate grid.

$y = 3x - 2$	
x	y
1	$1
2	$4
3	$7
4	$10

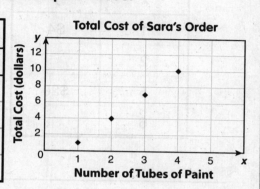

Total Cost of Sara's Order

Trading cards cost $1 each. The equation $y = 10 - 1x$ shows how much change Sylvester will receive (y) if he buys x cards with a $10 bill.

1. Copy and complete the function table.

$y = 10 - x$	
x	y
1	$9
2	$8
3	
4	

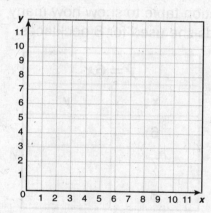

2. Write the ordered pairs. _____

3. Plot the points on the coordinate grid.

Spiral Review (Chapter 16, Lesson 2) **SDAP 1.1, SDAP 1.2**

4. Find the median: 12, 18, 16, 10, 18, 14, 10

5. Find the mode: 13, 21, 17, 23, 11, 13, 15, 19

6. Brooke received these quiz scores 86, 54, 90, 81, 74. What is her mean score?

_____   _____   _____

Name _____ Date _____

Graphs of Functions

Solve.

1. Complete the function table to find the cost of cupcakes if each box costs $4.

x	y
1	$4
2	
5	$20
6	

_____

2. Complete the function table to find the number of pictures on 10 pages if each page holds 5 pictures.

x	y
1	5
2	10
3	15
10	

_____

3. Brianna placed 6 beads on each necklace she made. Complete the function table to show how many beads she used for 8 necklaces.

y = 6x	
x	y
6	
7	
8	

_____

4. Cassie placed 4 photographs on each page of her photo album. The equation $y = 4x$ shows the number of photographs she has in her album (y) if it has x pages. How many photographs are in the album if it has 10 pages?

_____

5. Devin had $10 to purchase slices of pizza for himself and his friends. The slices of pizza cost $2 each. The equation $y = 10 - 2x$ shows how much change Devin will receive (y) if he buys different numbers of slices of pizza (x) with a $10 bill. Solve for y if x = 5.

_____

6. The book store was selling chapter books for $5 each and providing $3 off the entire purchase. The equation $y = 5x - 3$ shows the total purchase price (y) for buying a different number of chapter books (x) with $3 off the entire purchase. Solve for y if x = 8.

_____

Name _____ Date _____

Graphs from Patterns

CA Standards
AF 1.0, **KEY** AF 1.5

Justin made the pattern below using trapezoids. How can Justin graph the function to find the number of trapezoids in Figure 5 if the pattern continues?

Figure 1   Figure 2   Figure 3

  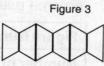

Step **1** Make a function table for Figures 1–3. Then graph the ordered pairs on the coordinate grid.

Figure Number	Number of Trapezoids
x	y
1	2
2	4
3	6

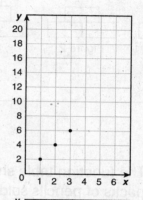

Step **2** The number of trapezoids is 2 times the Figure Number, so the equation for this function is $y = 2x$. Use this equation or extend the graph to find the number of trapezoids in Figure 5.

Solution: There are 10 trapezoids in Figure 5.

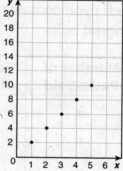

Use the equation or extend the graph to find the number of trapezoids in each figure.

1. Figure 6   **2.** Figure 8   **3.** Figure 12   **4.** Figure 20

_____   _____   _____   _____

Spiral Review (Chapter 16, Lesson 2) **SDAP 1.1, SDAP 1.2**

5. Find the mode: 15, 17, 19, 19, 17, 14, 18, 19 _____

6. Find the median: 25, 29, 20, 14, 19, 21, 28, 27 _____

7. Kelvin's spelling test scores are shown below. What is his mean score? _____

78, 45, 31, 90, 76, 100

Homework
163
Use with text pp. 374–375

Graphs from Patterns

CA Standards
AF 1.0, KEY AF 1.5

Solve problems 1–6.

1. If the pattern continues, how many blocks will there be in Figure 4?

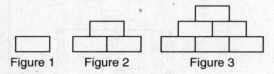

Figure 1   Figure 2   Figure 3

_____

2. Rachael drew dots to make a pattern. Use the function table to write the ordered pairs.

Figure Number	x	1	2	3	4
Number of Dots	y	4	8	12	16

_____

_____

3. The function table shows the number of packs of pencils sold at the school store. Each pack contains 6 pencils. Write the ordered pairs.

Number of Packs Sold	Total Number of Pencils Sold
x	y
1	6
2	12
3	18

_____

4. The function table shows how many juice boxes were sold. The juice boxes come in packages of 3. Choose the equation for the function.

Number of Packages Sold	Total Number of Juice Boxes Sold
x	y
5	15
6	18
7	21

A $y = x + 3$ **B** $y = 3x$ **C** $y = x - 3$

5. Maria made this pattern using dots. If she continues the pattern, how many dots will be in Figure 10?

Figure 1   Figure 2   Figure 3   Figure 4

_____

6. Betsy used tiles to make a pattern with 3, 5, 7, 9, and 11 squares. Find the ordered pair for the number of squares in Figure 10.

_____

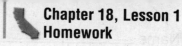
Hands On: Measure and Draw Angles

CA Standards
KEY MG 2.1, MR 2.2

You can use a protractor to measure an angle.

Step ① Place the center mark of the protractor on the vertex of the angle.

Step ② Align the 0° mark of one of the protractor scales with one ray of the angle.

Step ③ Find where the other ray passes through the scale and read the two numbers.

Step ④ If the angle is greater than 90°, use the greater number for your measurement. If the angle is less than 90°, use the lesser number for your measurement.

Estimate the measure of each angle. Then, use a protractor to measure each angle. Write the measure.

1.
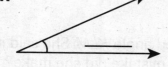

2.
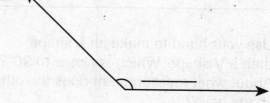

3.
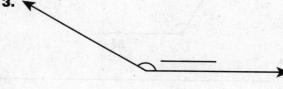

4.
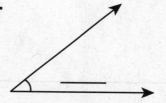

Use a protractor to draw an angle having each measure.

5. 15°   **6.** 130°

7. 180°   **8.** 60°

Spiral Review (Chapter 14, Lesson 2) **KEY** NS 2.1, **KEY** NS 2.2

Find each quotient. Multiply to check your answer.

9. 3)2.4 _____   **10.** 6)18.6 _____   **11.** 2)0.32 _____

12. A piece of string 11.2 feet long is cut into 4 equal pieces. What is the length of each piece of string? _____

Hands On: Measure and Draw Angles

CA Standards
KEY MG 2.1, MR 2.2

Solve.

1. Simone needed to draw a 90° angle, but she left her protractor at school. What could she use to help her draw the angle? Explain.

_____

_____

_____

2. Helena is doing her homework. She is supposed to find combinations of different angles that she can add to make straight lines. What should be the total measurement of each set of angles that combines for a straight line?

3. Use your hand to make an **L** shape, then a **V** shape. Which is closer to 90°? About what measurement does the other shape have?

_____

_____

4. Marie measured angle *KLM*. She said it was 60°. What mistake did she make?

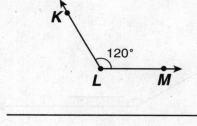

_____

_____

_____

_____

5. If you drew a circle and divided it into equal parts by drawing five lines through the center point, how many angles would you form at the center point? What would each angle measure?

_____

_____

6. In Problem 5, the angles formed at the center point are *central angles*. Ramona said that there is an infinite number of possible central angles in a circle. Is she correct? Explain.

_____

_____

Classify Angles

CA Standard
KEY MG 2.1

Classifying Angles

Right angle: the measure is equal to 90°

Acute angle: the measure is greater than 0° and less than 90°

Obtuse angle: the measure is greater than 90° and less than 180°

Straight angle: the measure is equal to 180°

Classify each angle as *acute, obtuse, straight,* or *right*.

1.
120°

_____

2.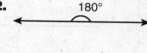
180°

_____

3.
60°

_____

4.
90°

_____

Use a protractor to measure each angle. Write the measure. Classify each angle as acute, obtuse, straight, or right.

5.

_____

6.

_____

7.

_____

8.

_____

Spiral Review   (Chapter 14, Lesson 3) **KEY** NS 2.1

Write each quotient as a decimal number. Multiply to check.

9. 5)9   _____

10. 2)13   _____

11. 4)18   _____

12. Anna spent 15 minutes covering 4 textbooks. If she spent the same amount of time on each textbook, how long did it take her to cover one textbook?

_____

Classify Angles

Solve.

1. List these angle types in order from smallest to largest: obtuse, straight, right, acute.

   _____

   _____

2. Susan says this angle is a right angle. Jeremy says it's acute. Who is correct, or are they both wrong? Explain. (Remember that angles measuring less than 90° are acute, and angles measuring greater than 90° are obtuse.)

   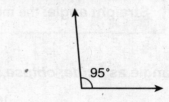

   _____

   _____

   _____

3. What two angles would you get if you split a right angle in half? Tell the measure and classify the angles.

   _____

4. Classify the five angles marked in this quadrilateral.

   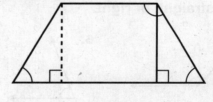

   _____

   _____

5. What is another way to read an angle on a protractor?

   _____

   _____

   _____

   _____

6. Which is greater, the measure of a straight angle plus an acute angle, or the measure of two obtuse angles? Explain, with examples.

   _____

   _____

   _____

   _____

Lines and Line Segments

Parallel lines or line segments never intersect.

Intersecting lines or line segments cross at one point.

Perpendicular lines or line segments form right (90°) angles when they intersect.

Draw each pair of lines.

1. Line $\overleftrightarrow{GH}$ and line $\overleftrightarrow{WX}$ intersecting at point L.

2. Line $\overleftrightarrow{MN}$ perpendicular to line $\overleftrightarrow{XY}$.

3. Line $\overleftrightarrow{LP}$ parallel to line $\overleftrightarrow{CD}$.

4. Line $\overleftrightarrow{PQ}$ parallel to line $\overleftrightarrow{DG}$.

Draw each pair of line segments.

5. Line segment $\overline{LM}$ perpendicular to line segment $\overline{NP}$.

6. Line segment $\overline{BK}$ and line segment $\overline{JN}$ intersecting at point X.

Spiral Review (Chapter 14, Lesson 4) **KEY** NS 2.1

Divide. Check your answers.

7. $0.3\overline{)27}$ _____

8. $0.05\overline{)15}$ _____

9. $0.2\overline{)64}$ _____

10. A bus traveled 30 miles in 0.6 hour. What was the speed of the bus?

_____

Lines and Line Segments

CA Standard
KEY MG 2.1, MR 2.3

Solve.

1. Is $\overleftrightarrow{AB}$ a line or a line segment? Remember: a line is shown with two arrows. A line segment is shown with two endpoints.

$\overset{\bullet}{A} \qquad\qquad \overset{\bullet}{B}$

_____

2. Michele said that this figure should be labeled $\overleftrightarrow{FE}$. Is she right or wrong? If she is wrong, what should she write instead?

$\overset{\bullet}{F} \qquad\qquad \overset{\bullet}{E}$

_____
_____
_____

3. Gemma is making rectangles from parallel and perpendicular line segments. She drew four parallel line segments, then added three more line segments perpendicular to the first four. What is the greatest number of rectangles she could have formed?

_____

4. Marco said that all perpendicular lines are intersecting lines, but not all intersecting lines are perpendicular. Is he correct? Explain.

_____
_____
_____
_____
_____

5. Which of these—a line, line segment, or ray—can contain the other two figures?

_____
_____
_____
_____

6. Mrs. Peters asked her students to draw figures that had exactly two perpendicular line segments. Kelly drew a triangle, and said that 3 was the greatest number of sides possible. Patrick drew a 4-sided figure and said that 4 was the greatest number of sides possible. Who is correct? Explain.

_____
_____

Hands On: Sums of Angle Measures

CA Standards
KEY MG 2.2, **KEY** MG 2.1

Find the sum of the measures of the angles in a triangle.

Step ① Use a straightedge to draw any triangle.
Cut it out. Label the angles *a*, *b*, and *c*.
Make triangle different from the one in Reteach.
Place triangle to the right of the Steps.

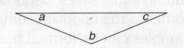

Step ② Tear off the three angles of the triangle.

Step ③ Use a straightedge to draw a straight angle.
Arrange the angles of the triangle so they
meet at a point and lie on the straight angle.

The sum of the measures of the angles in a triangle is 180°.

Find the sum of the measures of the angles in a quadrilateral.

1. Use a straightedge to draw any quadrilateral. Label the angles *a*, *b*, *c*, and *d*.

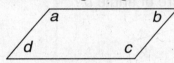

2. On your quadrilateral, draw a line segment connecting one vertex to the opposite vertex. Cut the quadrilateral along the line you drew. Place the pieces together to fit into your original quadrilateral.

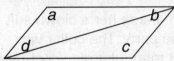

3. What is the sum of the measures of the angles in a quadrilateral?

_____

Spiral Review (Chapter 15, Lesson 5) **KEY NS 2.2**

Solve.

4. $1,305 \div 15$ _____

5. $12,450 \div 30$ _____

6. Barbara's Bakery baked 25,248 cookies. One cookie bag holds 24 cookies. How many bags will the bakery need to use to hold all of the cookies?

_____

Name _____ Date _____

Hands On: Sums of Angle Measures

CA Standards
KEY MG.2.2, KEY MG 2.1

Solve.

1. In art class, Becky is making a design by cutting square tiles diagonally from one corner to the opposite corner. How many triangles can be formed from one square tile?

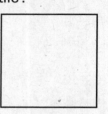

_____

2. Julian is also making a design using rectangular tiles. How many triangles can be formed by cutting a rectangular tile from corner to corner?

_____

3. Brett drew the triangle below. What is the measure of angle z?

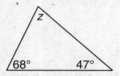

_____

4. Raul drew the quadrilateral below. What is the measure of angle d?

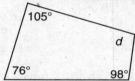

_____

5. How many quadrilaterals form this figure? Name the types of quadrilaterals. What is the sum of the measure of the angles of the quadrilaterals?

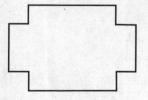

_____

_____

6. Alison's mom made her a clown suit for a costume party. The collar was made from 8 triangular pieces of fabric. What is the sum of the measure of the angles of the triangles used to make her costume?

_____

Triangles

CA Standards
KEY MG 2.2, MG 2.0

Classify the triangle by its angle measures.

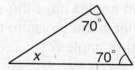

Step 1 70° + 70° = 140°

Step 2 180° − 140° = 40°, so $x = 40°$

Step 3 The measures of the angles of this triangle are less than 90°, so they are acute.

Solution: This is an acute triangle.

Classify the triangle by the length of its sides.

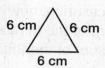

Step 1 The lengths of all three sides are 6 cm.

Step 2 All of the sides are the same length, so the triangle is equilateral.

Solution: This is an equilateral triangle.

Classify each triangles in two ways.

1. 35 miles, 16 miles, 16 miles

_____

2. 7 in., 9 in., 11.4 in.

_____

3. 6 m, 8 m, 7 m

_____

Find the missing angle measure.

4.
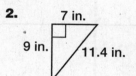
x, 55°

_____

5.
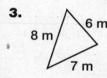
60°, 60°, x

_____

6.
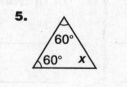
25°, x, 35°

_____

Spiral Review (Chapter 15, Lesson 5) **KEY** NS 2.2

Solve.

7. 2,415 ÷ 23 = _____

8. 44,688 ÷ 76 = _____

9. A vehicle manufacturer delivered 50,484 new trucks to 84 dealerships in the United States. Each dealership received the same number of trucks. How many trucks did each dealership receive?

Name _____ Date _____

Triangles

CA Standards
KEY MG 2.2, MG 2.0

Solve.

1. Mavis has found the measures of two angles of a triangle: 72° and 47°. Without measuring, how can she find the measure of the third angle? What is the measure of the third angle?

_____

_____

2. Kan measured the angles of an isosceles triangle. One angle measure is 36°. The other two angles have the same measure. What is the measure of each of the two other angles?

_____

3. What triangles are formed when you draw a line down the middle of an equilateral triangle?

_____

4. Use the clues to find the angle measures of the following triangle:
   - The second angle is double the measure of the first angle.
   - The third angle is the sum of the other two angle measures.

_____

5. Can the measure of an angle in an equilateral triangle be anything other than 60°? Explain.

_____

_____

_____

_____

_____

6. Mike says that every triangle has to have an obtuse angle. Is he correct? Use an example or drawing to explain.

_____

_____

_____

_____

_____

Quadrilaterals

CA Standards
KEY MG 2.2, MG 2.0

Missing Angle Measure

Find the measure of $\angle QRS$.

Subtract the sum of the known angle measures from 360°.

Step 1 $\angle QRS = 360° - (72° + 118° + 90°)$

Step 2 $\angle QRS = 360° - 280° = 80°$

Solution: $\angle QRS = 80°$

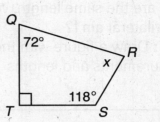

Classify each figure in as many ways as possible. Then find the missing angle measure.

1.
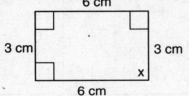
6 cm
3 cm   3 cm
x
6 cm

_____

_____

2.
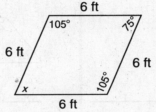
6 ft
105°   75°
6 ft   6 ft
105°
x
6 ft

_____

_____

3.
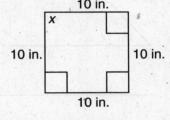
10 in.
x
10 in.   10 in.
10 in.

_____

_____

Spiral Review (Chapter 16, Lesson 3) **KEY** SDAP 1.4

Use the line graph for Problems 4–6.

4. How many more cars than trucks were sold in March?

_____

5. During which month were sales for both cars and trucks the same?

_____

6. Between which two months was there the greatest decrease in sales of cars?

_____

_____

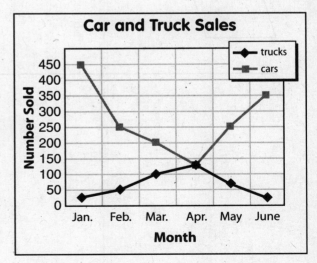

Car and Truck Sales

Quadrilaterals

Solve.

1. I have four right angles and my opposite sides are the same length. Which quadrilateral am I?
HINT: Draw a figure with these angles measurements and lengths

_____

2. All four of my sides are the same length and my opposite sides are parallel. Which quadrilateral am I?
HINT: Draw a figure with these lengths.

_____

3. The measure of two angles of this parallelogram are 105° and 75°. Find the measure of angles x and y.

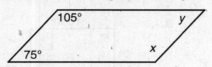

_____

4. Three angles of a quadrilateral have measures of 107°, 83°, and 75°. What is the measure of angle z?

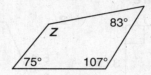

_____

5. The measure of one angle of a rhombus is 60°. Find the measure of the three missing angles.

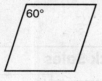

_____

6. Using what you know about classifying quadrilaterals, explain how a quadrilateral could be classified as a rhombus but not as a square.

_____

_____

_____

_____

_____

_____

Congruence

Johnny is building two bookshelves. Figures *RSTP* and *VWUZ* are two pieces of wood he has. Are *RSTP* and *VWUZ* congruent?

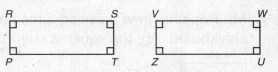

Use a Tracing

Step 1 Trace *RSTP*. Then place your tracing on top of figure *VWUZ*.

Step 2 The figures are the same size and shape, so they are congruent.

Solution: *RSTP* ≅ *VWUZ*

Use a Ruler and Protractor

Step 1 Use a ruler to measure the sides of both figures. Then use a protractor to measure the angles both figures.

Step 2 The sides and angles are the same, so the figures are congruent.

Solution: *RSTP* ≅ *VWUZ*

In Problems 1 and 2, trace Figure 1. Use your tracing to determine if Figure 2 is congruent to Figure 1. Write *yes* or *no*.

1.

Figure 2

Figure 1

2. Figure 1   Figure 2

Use a ruler to measure the sides and a protractor to measure the angles. Determine if the two figures are congruent. Write *yes* or *no*.

3.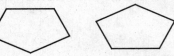

_____

4.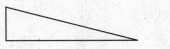

_____

Spiral Review (Chapter 18, Lessons 1 and 3) **KEY MG 2.1**

Use the diagram to answer Problem 5–6.

5. What is the length of side $\overline{VW}$?

_____

6. What is the measure of ∠*V*?

_____

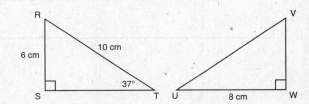

Congruence

CA Standards
KEY MG 2.1, MG 2.0

Solve.

1. Mr. Hopkins drew these squares on the chalkboard. Are the squares congruent?

4.5 in.

4.5 in.

4.2 in.

4.2 in.

_____

2. Mr. Boyer cut a 12-foot piece of wood into the pieces shown below. Are the pieces congruent?

_____

3. Which parts of the United States flag are congruent?

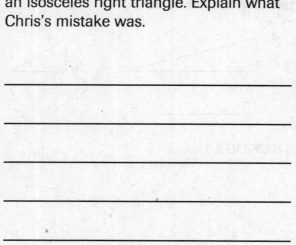

_____

_____

4. Stacey says that every design on the Australian flag and the New Zealand flag is congruent. Is she correct?

Australian flag

New Zealand flag

_____

_____

5. Chris said that the only triangle that has all congruent sides and angles is an isosceles right triangle. Explain what Chris's mistake was.

_____

_____

_____

_____

6. Mrs. Smith copied a worksheet for her math class. She reduced the original size of the worksheet by 50%. Are the copies congruent to the original worksheet? Explain.

_____

_____

_____

_____

Problem Solving: Missing Angle Problems

CA Standards
MR 2.3, **KEY** MG 2.2

In Frank's garden, green beans grow up a support in the shape of an isosceles triangle. If the support meets at a 20° angle, what are the measures of the other two angles?

Subtract the measure of the angle you know from 180°. Divide the difference by 2.

$$\begin{array}{r} 180° \\ - 20° \\ \hline 140° \end{array} \qquad 140° \div 2 = 70°$$

Solution: The angles at the ground measure 70° each.

Solve. Explain why your answer makes sense.

1. Mr. Orson's store has an awning that is supported by rods coming out from the wall. The wall, awning, and supporting rods form a right triangle. One of the angles of the triangle is 60°. What are the measures of the other angles?

   _____

   _____

2. Helena's door has a stained glass window shaped like a parallelogram. One corner of the window is an 80° angle. What are the measures of the other three angles in the window?

   _____

   _____

Spiral Review (Chapter 18, Lesson 3) **KEY** MG 2.1, MR 2.3

Describe each pair of lines using the appropriate symbols.

3.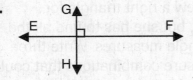

   _____

4.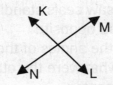

   _____

5. The double yellow lines that are painted on streets could be described as what type of

   lines? _____

Problem Solving: Missing Angle Problems

CA Standards
KEY MG 2.2, MR 2.3

Solve. Explain why your answer makes sense.

1. Bethany's herb garden is shaped like an equilateral triangle. What are the angle measures of the garden?
Hint: an equilateral triangle has three equal sides and three equal angles.

_____

_____

_____

2. The tree, rope, and ground in the picture form a right triangle. If one angle of the triangle is 30°, what are the other two angle measures? Remember that a right triangle has one right angle.

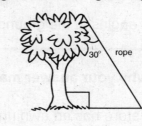

_____

_____

_____

3. Edwin hikes through the woods, starting and ending at his back door. He turns three times, so that his path takes the shape of a quadrilateral. The angles of his turns measure 80°, 130° and 100°. What angle is formed when he reaches his starting point?

_____

_____

4. John is drawing a parallelogram. One angle measures 120°. What are the measures of the other three angles?

_____

_____

_____

5. At the circus, Shawn saw seals standing on a trapezoid that had opposite sides equal. If one of the angles of the trapezoid was 135°, what were the other three angle measurements?

_____

_____

_____

6. Isabella drew a right triangle for homework, but she has to find all the possible angle measures. Write three angle measure combinations that could be possible for a right triangle.

_____

_____

_____

Name _____ Date _____

Hands On: Construct Parallel and Perpendicular Lines

CA Standards
KEY MG 2.1, MG 2.0

Construct line *k* so that *k* is parallel to a given line *h*, and passes through point *D* that is not on line *h*.

• *D*

Step ① Construct line *m* through point *D* perpendicular to *h* where *D* is not on *h*.

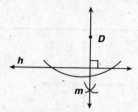

Line *h* and line *m* are perpendicular.

Step ② Construct line *k* through point *D* perpendicular to *m* where *D* is on *m*.

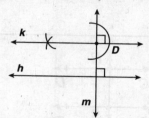

Line *h* and line *k* are parallel.

Use a compass for Problems 1–3.

1. Draw line *p*. Label a point *F* that is not on *p*. Construct line *q* so that *q* is perpendicular to *p* and passes through *F*.

2. Draw line *b*. Label a point *A* that is on *b*. Construct line *c* so that *c* is parallel to *b*.

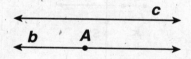

Spiral Review (Chapter 19, Lesson 2) **KEY** MG 2.2

Classify each triangle in two ways.

3.

4.

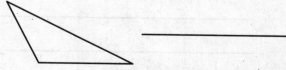

5. Jessica is making a design using the shape at the right. Classify the triangle in two ways.

Use with text pp. 430–431

Name _____ Date _____

Hands On: Construct Parallel and Perpendicular Lines

CA Standards
KEY MG 2.1, MG 2.0

Solve.

1. Which line below is parallel to $\overleftrightarrow{CD}$? Is it $\overleftrightarrow{AB}$ or $\overleftrightarrow{RS}$?

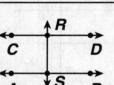

2. Karen said that perpendicular lines form 2 right angles. Dexter thinks Karen meant 4 right angles. Who is correct? Use the figure below to help.

3. Diane is drawing two perpendicular lines. First, she drew line d. What is the next step she should take?

_____

_____

4. Steve is constructing a line parallel to line r. The figure below is what he has drawn so far. What is the next step?

_____

_____

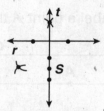

5. Brian drew the figure below. What are the relationships between the line segments?

_____

_____

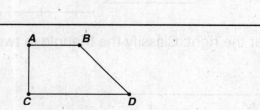

6. Marie drew this figure using parallel, perpendicular, and intersecting lines. Name the parallel lines.

_____

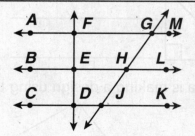

Hands On: Construct Triangles and Rectangles

Construct a rectangle, *PGHJ*, congruent to rectangle *STRE*.

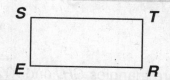

Step 1 Draw a line and label a point on the line *J*. Measure $\overline{ER}$. Using that measure, draw an arc from *J* and label the point of intersection *H*. Construct two lines that are perpendicular to $\overline{JH}$ at *J* and *H*. Label the points where the arcs intersect the line.

Step 2 Using the measure of $\overline{RT}$, draw an arc from *H* and label the point *G*. Draw an arc from *J* and label the point *P*. Draw $\overline{PG}$ to complete rectangle *PGHJ*.

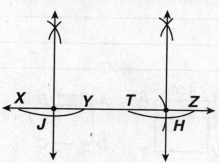

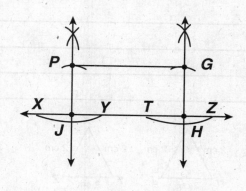

Complete the construction.

1. Construct a rectangle, *LMNP*, congruent to rectangle *DEFG*.

2. Construct a triangle, *RST*, congruent to equilateral triangle *XYZ*.

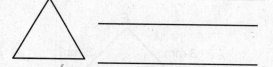

Spiral Review   (Chapter 19, Lesson 2) **KEY** MG 2.2

Classify each triangle in two ways.

3. _____

4. _____

Name _____ Date _____

Hands On: Construct Triangles and Rectangles

CA Standards
KEY MG 2.1, MR 2.0

Solve.

1. Are triangles *GHJ* and *XYZ* congruent? Explain.

_____

_____

_____

_____

_____

_____

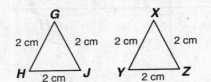

2. Square *RSTV* has a side length of 4 centimeters and square *ABCD* has a side length of 3 centimeters. George says the two squares are congruent. Is he correct? Explain.

_____

_____

_____

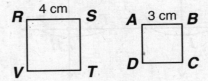

3. Marcus is constructing rectangle *LMNP* congruent to rectangle *ABCD*. What is his first step?

_____

_____

_____

```
A          B

D          C
```

4. Are all equilateral triangles congruent?

_____

_____

5. How could you construct triangle *CHM* if the only measurements you have are the angle measurements of 120°, 30°, and 30°?

_____

_____

6. Jackie drew triangle *DEF*. Explain how she can construct triangle *TPW* so *TPW* is double the size of *DEF*.

_____

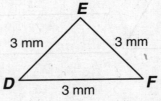

Perimeter and Area of Complex Figures

CA Standards
MG 1.0, **KEY** NS 2.1

Find the area and perimeter of the figure.

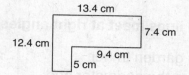

Step ① Divide the figure into simple figures. Draw a line that divides the figure into two rectangles.

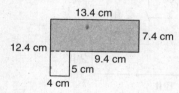

Step ③ Find the sum of the areas.

$A = 99.16$ cm² $+ 20$ cm²
$A = 119.16$ cm²

Step ② Use the formula to find the area of the rectangles.

large rectangle: $A = lw$
  $(13.4) \times (7.4)$ cm²
  99.16 cm²

small rectangle: $A = lw$
  $(5) \times (4)$ cm²
  20 cm²

Step ④ To find the perimeter of the figure, add the lengths of all the sides.

$P = 13.4 + 7.4 + 9.4 + 5 + 4 + 12.4$
$P = 51.6$ cm

Find the perimeter and area of the figure. All corners are right angles.

1.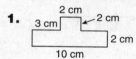

2.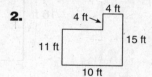

3.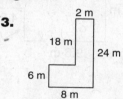

_____ _____ _____

(Chapter 19, Lesson 2) **KEY** MG 2.2

Classify each triangle in two ways.

4. 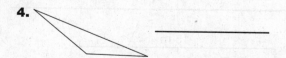 _____
_____

5. 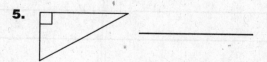 _____
_____

6. The top of a triangular table is shown below.
Classify the shape of the tabletop in two ways.

 _____

Name _____   Date _____

Perimeter and Area of Complex Figures

CA Standards
MG 1.0, KEY NS 2.1

Solve. All intersecting lines meet at right angles.

1. Lesli is planting a garden in her backyard. What are the perimeter and area of the garden?

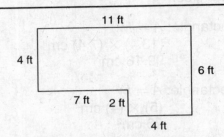

2. Rob is making a sandbox for his younger cousins. What are the perimeter and area of the sandbox?

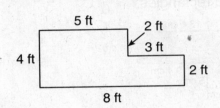

3. Jarrod is ordering stones to cover his patio. What are the perimeter and area of the patio?

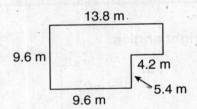

4. Meghan and Kim are laying a new tile floor in Meghan's kitchen. What are the perimeter and area of Meghan's kitchen?

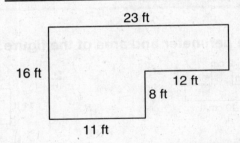

5. Shannon needs to find out how much carpet to buy for her bedroom. Will she need to find the area or perimeter of her bedroom floor? Explain your answer.

_____

_____

_____

_____

_____

_____

6. Sarita is helping her mother make a flower garden. They need to know how many seeds they will use and how many feet of wooden border to purchase. What are the perimeter and area of the flower garden?

_____

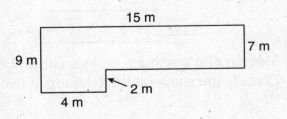

Problem Solving:
Multistep Problems

CA Standards
MR 1.2, MG 1.0

The figure shows the dimensions of a countertop that Paul has designed for his kitchen. The granite needed for his countertop costs $35.75 for 5 m². How much money will Paul spend on granite for his countertop?

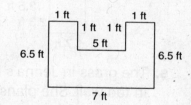

2 m
3 m
10 m
11 m
8 m
12 m

Step ❶ Divide the complex figure.

Step ❷ Find the area.
Area of Rectangle 1:
$A = l \times w$
$= 12 \text{ m} \times 8 \text{ m}$
$= 96 \text{ m}^2$
Area of Rectangle 2:
$A = l \times w$
$= 2 \text{ m} \times 3 \text{ m}$
$= 6 \text{ m}^2$
Find the sum of the areas to find the area of the entire countertop.
$A = 96 \text{ m}^2 + 6 \text{ m}^2$
$= 102 \text{ m}^2$

Step ❸ Find the cost of the granite.
5m² costs $35.75.
102 m² ÷ 5 m² = 20.4, or about 21
21 × $35.75 = $750.75

Solve. Explain why your answer makes sense.

1. Leslie is making the sign shown. She has enough paint to cover 40 ft². Is that enough paint to cover the front of the sign?

1 ft   1 ft
1 ft 1 ft
5 ft
6.5 ft   6.5 ft

7 ft

_____

_____

Spiral Review (Chapter 19, Lesson 2) **MG 2.0, KEY MG 2.2**

Classify each triangle in two ways.

2.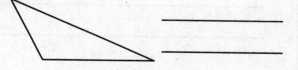

3.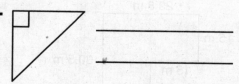

Problem Solving:
Multistep Problems

CA Standards
MR 1.2, MG 1.0

Solve. Explain why your answer makes sense.

1. The area of a wall is 52 ft². A can of paint that will cover 13 ft² costs $9.98. How much will paint cost to cover the wall?

$52 \div 13 =$ _____

_____ $\times 9.98 =$ _____

2. The perimeter of a complex figure is 128 m. Kelsey wants to place lighting around the border of the figure. She can buy the lighting in strands of 8 m. How many strands of lighting does she need to buy?

_____

_____

3. What is the area of the sandbox shown below?

_____

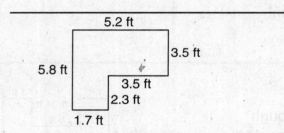

4. Use the figure in Problem 3. Tony wants to place a fence around the sandbox. A roll of fencing is 4 feet long. How many rolls of fencing should he buy?

_____

5. The grass in Jenna's lawn has not grown in too well. She plans to throw more seed onto her lawn. A 1-lb bag of seed costs $22 and covers 60 m². A 5-lb bag of seed costs $88 and covers 300 m². How much will Jenna spend on grass seed for her lawn?

_____

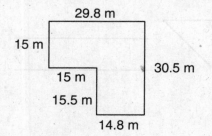

6. Use the figure in Problem 5. Jenna wants to build a fence around her yard. She has 75 meters of fence. How many more meters of fence does she need to buy?

_____

_____

_____

Hands On: Area of Parallelograms

CA Standards
KEY MG 1.1, MG 1.0

Find the area of the parallelogram shown.

Step ① Copy the parallelogram. Draw the height *h* to make a triangle. Shade the triangle shape on the end of the figure. Cut out the triangle.

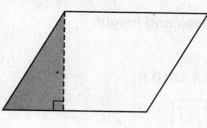

Step ② Move the cut-out triangle to the other side of the parallelogram and tape it in place to form a rectangle. Determine the height and length of the rectangle and multiply together.

$A = 9 \text{ cm} \times 7 \text{ cm}$
$A = 63 \text{ cm}^2$

Copy each parallelogram onto centimeter grid paper. Draw a line perpendicular to the other side to make a triangle. Cut out each parallelogram. Then cut off the triangular piece. Make the parallelogram into a rectangle.

1. 7 cm 12 cm _____

2. 5 cm 3 cm _____

3. 4 ft 20 ft _____

Spiral Review (Chapter 16, Lesson 4) AF 1.1

Kim's Allowance Spending

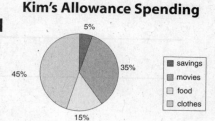

Use the information from the graph to solve the problems.

4. Is more money spent on movies or clothes?

_____

5. Which two categories make up half of Kim's spending?

_____

Name _____ Date _____

Area of Parallelograms

Find the area of the parallelograms in 1 & 2.

1.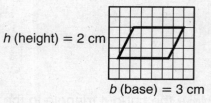
h (height) = 2 cm
b (base) = 3 cm

_____

2.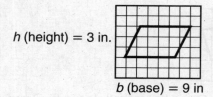
h (height) = 3 in.
b (base) = 9 in

_____

Draw each parallelogram on the grids provided. Label the base and height. Find the area of each parallelogram.

3. $b = 7$ cm; $h = 3$ cm

_____

4. $b = 6$ ft; $h = 10$ ft

_____

5. If a parallelogram has an area of 91 ft² and its height is 7 ft, what is the length of its base? Explain.

_____

_____

6. A parallelogram has a base of 22 ft and a height of 15 ft. Is the area of that parallelogram greater than, less than, or equal to the area of a rectangle with a length of 15 ft and a width of 22 ft? Explain.

_____

_____

_____

Name _____ Date _____

Area of Parallelograms

CA Standards
KEY MG 1.1, MG 1.0

A = bh
= 8.5 × 4
= 34
The area is 34 square centimeters or 34 cm².

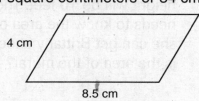

4 cm

8.5 cm

Find the area of each figure.

1.
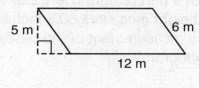
5 m   6 m
12 m

2.
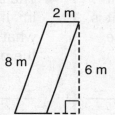
2 m
8 m
6 m

3.
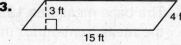
3 ft   4 ft
15 ft

_____   _____   _____

4.
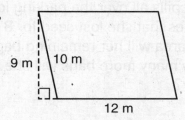
9 m   10 m
12 m

5.
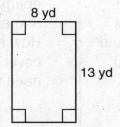
8 yd
13 yd

6.
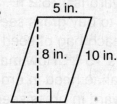
5 in.
8 in.   10 in.

_____   _____   _____

Spiral Review (Chapter 16, Lesson 4) AF 1.1

Don's Time Spent on Homework

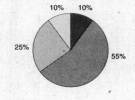

■ math
□ reading
□ science
■ social studies

10% 10%
25%
55%

Use the information from the graph to solve the problems.

7. Which two subjects does Don spend the same amount of time on?

_____

8. Which subject takes up more than half of his homework time?

_____

Area of Parallelograms

Solve problems 1–6.

1. If the base of a parallelogram measures 14 cm and the height measures 9 cm. What is the area of the parallelogram?

_____

2. Brittany is designing a mural in the shape of a parallelogram. The base of the parallelogram will be 21 feet and the height will be 10 feet. The art teacher needs to know the area of the mural so she can get Brittany enough paint. What is the area of the mural?

_____

3. The area of a parallelogram is 153.6 in². The base measures 19.2 inches. What is the measurement for the height of the parallelogram?

_____

4. The area of a parallelogram is 1,228.15 in². If the height measures 60.5 inches, what is the measurement of the base of the parallelogram?

_____

5. Janae's backyard is in the shape of a parallelogram. The area of Janae's backyard is 175.2 ft². She goes to the store to buy grass seed and discovers that each bag of seed costs $32.89 and covers 15 ft². How many bags of seed will Janae need in order to cover her backyard in grass seed?

_____

6. Use problem 5. As Janae is loading the bags of grass seed into her car a bag opens and spills all over the parking lot. She estimates that she lost seed for 8 ft². How much area will her remaining bags cover? How many more bags will she need to buy?

_____

_____

Hands On: Area of Triangles

CA Standards
KEY MG 1.1, MG 1.0

Use a parallelogram to find the area of a triangle.

**Step ① ** Find the area of the parallelogram.

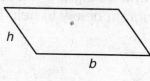

$b = $ 4 cm
$h = $ 2 cm

$A = bh$

$A = 4 \times 2 = 8$ cm²

Solution: The triangle has an area of 4 cm².

**Step ② ** Make two triangles and find the area. A line from a vertex to the vertex opposite it makes two equal triangles.

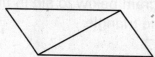

The area of a triangle is one half the area of a parallelogram.

So, $A = \frac{1}{2} (b \times h)$ or $A = \frac{1}{2} bh$.

Make two copies of each triangle on the same piece of grid paper. Cut out one copy. Place it besides the uncut copy to make a parallelogram. Find the area of the parallelogram. Find the area of the triangle.

1.

5 m h
5 m

2.

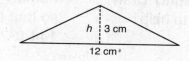

h 3 cm
12 cm

3.

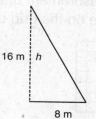

16 m h
8 m

_____ _____ _____

_____ _____ _____

Spiral Review (Chapter 20, Lesson 3) MG 1.0

Find the perimeter and area of each figure.

4.

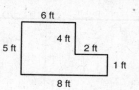

6 ft
5 ft   4 ft
2 ft
1 ft
8 ft

5.

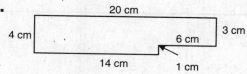

20 cm
4 cm   3 cm
6 cm
14 cm   1 cm

_____ _____

_____ _____

Hands On: Area of Triangles

Solve problems 1–6.

1. If the base of a parallelogram measures 5 cm and the height of the parallelogram measures 6 cm, what would be the area of one of the triangles? Use the parallelogram below to aid in finding the area of the triangle.

_____

2. What is the area of a triangle with a base of 12 ft and a height of 6.5 ft? Use the parallelogram below to help find the area.

_____

3. The area of a triangle is 18 cm². If the base of the triangle is 4 cm, what would be the measurement of the height? Draw the triangle on the grid below to help.

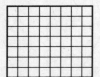

_____

4. The base of a triangle is the same as its height. What are the least whole number measurements for the triangle so that the area would be greater than 144 ft²?

_____

5. Katie made a kite by sewing two congruent triangles together to form a parallelogram. The base of each triangle is 13 in. and the height is 6 in. What is the area of Katie's kite?

_____

6. Katie also made a kite out of 4 congruent triangles which when sewn together make two parallelograms. The base of each triangle is 7.3 cm and the height is 9 cm. What is the area of Katie's kite?

_____

194

Area of a Triangles

CA Standards
KEY MG 1.1, MG 1.0

Find the area of a triangle with a base of 8 cm and a height of 6 cm.

$A = \dfrac{1}{2} \times b \times h$ $\qquad$ $A = \dfrac{1}{2} \times 8 \times 6$ $\qquad$ $A = 24 \text{ cm}^2$

Find the area of each triangle.

1.
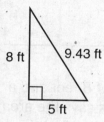
8 ft   9.43 ft   5 ft

_____

2.
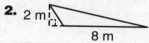
2 m   8 m

_____

3.
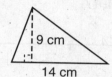
9 cm   14 cm

_____

4.
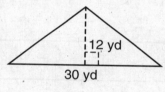
12 yd   30 yd

_____

5.

8 m   4 m

_____

6.
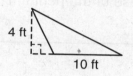
4 ft   10 ft

_____

Spiral Review   (Chapter 20, Lesson 3) **KEY NS 2.1**

Find the area of each figure

7.
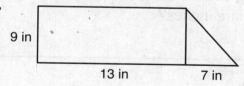
9 in   13 in   7 in

_____

8.
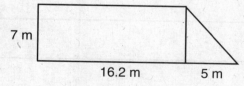
7 m   16.2 m   5 m

_____

9. An artist is making a giant rectangular mural for a high school gym. The rectangle will have a 43-foot base. If the mural will be 16 feet tall, how many square feet of wall space will the mural use?

_____

Name _____ Date _____

Area of Triangles

Solve problems 1–6.

1. The teachers at Jefferson Elementary handed out triangle–shaped pennants on the first day of school. If each pennant has a base of 5 inches and a height of 12 inches, what is the area of each pennant?

   _____

2. On the first day of school, students also received a triangle locker tag. If the base of the triangle is 4 in. and the height is 6 in., what is the area of the locker tag?

   _____

3. The high school also sells a small pennant. If the small pennant has a height of 24 inches and the area is 108 square inches what is the length of the base of the pennant?

   _____

4. A triangle has a base of 8 feet and a height of 6 feet. Beatrix says the area of the triangle is 48 square feet. Explain what Beatrix's mistake was. Then tell the correct answer.

   _____

   _____

   _____

5. How are the area formulas of triangles and parallelograms alike? How are they different?

   _____

   _____

   _____

   _____

6. At football games, the local high school sells large pennants. If each pennant has a base of 1 foot and height of 2.5 feet, what is the area of each pennant in square inches?

   _____

   _____

Hands On: Make Solids Using Nets

CA Standard
KEY MG 1.2

Karen is making pieces for a board game. Which type of net is she using?

Step Copy the net. Then cut it out.

Step ② Fold the net on the dotted lines. Tape the edges together.

Solution: Karen is using a net for a cube to make the game pieces.

Predict whether the net forms a rectangular prism, a cube, or neither. Then copy the pattern onto grid paper, cut it out, fold it, and tape it together to check your prediction.

1.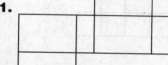

_____

2.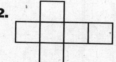

_____

3.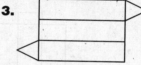

_____

Spiral Review (Chapter 19, Lesson 3) **KEY** MG 2.2

Classify each figure in as many ways as possible. Then find the missing angle measures.

4.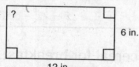

6 in.
12 in.

_____

5. Jessica is making a design using the shape below. Classify the figure in two ways.

120°
?

_____

6. Julio is making a tabletop in the shape shown below. What shape is this? What is the missing angle?

?

_____

Use with text pp. 472–473

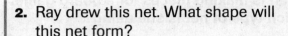
Hands On: Make Solids Using Nets

CA Standard
KEY MG 1.2

Solve problems 1–6.

1. Nicky has to fold this box. When Nicky folds this box, what shape will be formed?

_____

2. Ray drew this net. What shape will this net form?

_____

3. This net has 4 large rectangles and 2 small rectangles. Which solid figure will it form?

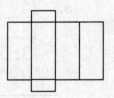

_____

4. Ellis drew this net for a cube. Explain his mistake. Then tell what the net should look like.

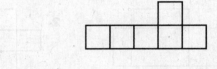

_____

_____

_____

_____

5. Draw a net for a square pyramid. What shapes are needed to form this figure?

_____

_____

6. Ken ate a bowl of cereal for breakfast. Draw the net that would form a box of cereal.

Hands On: Draw Views of Solid figures

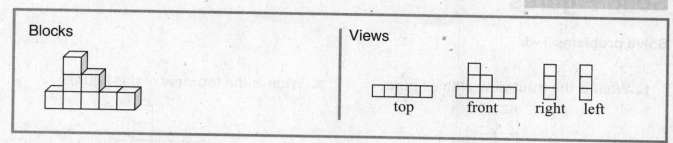

Blocks | Views | top | front | right | left

Use cubes to build each figure. Then draw a top view, a front view, a right side view, and a left side view of the figure on grid paper.

1.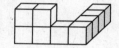

2.   _____

_____

Draw the figure for each set of views.

3.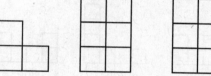

4.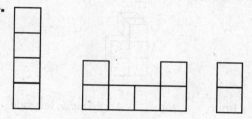

Spiral Review   (Chapter 19, Lesson 3) **KEY** MG 2.2

Classify each figure in as many ways as possible. Then find the missing angle measures.

5.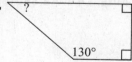

_____

6.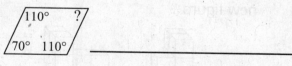

_____

_____

7. Susanna is making a quilt and cut this shape out of fabric. What is the shape? What is the missing angle?

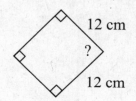

12 cm
?
12 cm

_____

_____

Hands On: Draw Views of Solid Figures

CA Standards
MG 2.3, MG 2.0

Solve problems 1–6.

1. What is the front view of this figure?

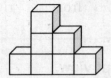

2. What is the top view of this figure?

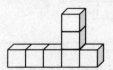

3. Draw the front, top, right side, and left side view of the figure.

front   top   right side   left side

4. Draw a three-dimensional figure using these views.

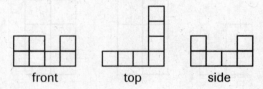

front   top   side

5. Combine the two figures below. Then draw a front, top, and side view of your new figure.

6. Mr. Donald built a staircase that measured 3 cubic units wide and has a height of 5 cubic units. Draw a sketch of the staircase.

Surface Area

CA Standards
MG 1.0, KEY MG 1.2

What is the surface area of the box?

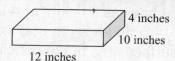

4 inches
10 inches
12 inches

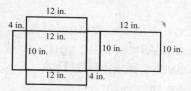

Step 1 Find the number of faces on the rectangular prism.

Step 2 Complete the table to find the area of each face.

Face	Length	Width	Area	Face	Length	Width	Area
top	12	10	120 in²	left side	10	4	40 in²
bottom	12	10	120 in²	right side	10	4	40 in²
front	12	4	48 in²				
back	12	4	48 in²			sum:	416 in²

Add the areas to find the surface area.

Solution: The surface area is 416 in².

Predict what solid figure each net will make. Then find the surface area of the figure.

1.

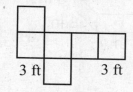

2 cm
4 cm
2 cm   8 cm

_____
_____
_____

2.

3 ft   3 ft

_____

Spiral Review (Chapter 19, Lesson 3) **KEY MG 2.2**

Classify each figure in as many ways as possible. Then find the missing angle measures.

3.

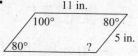

11 in.
100°   80°
80°   ?   5 in.

_____

_____

4.

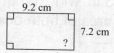

9.2 cm
7.2 cm
?

_____

_____

5. Bill is tiling the floor in his bathroom with tiles like this one. What is the shape of this tile? What is the missing angle?

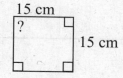

15 cm
?
15 cm

_____

_____

Surface Area

CA Standards
MG 1.0, **KEY** MG 1.2

Solve problems 1–6.

1. Tina's jewelry box is in the shape of a rectangular prism. What is the surface area of Tina's jewelry box? **HINT:** A rectangular prism has 6 faces.

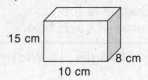

15 cm
8 cm
10 cm

_____

2. Grace's pencil box has a height of 4 in., a length of 11 in., and a width of 6 in. What is the surface area of the pencil box?

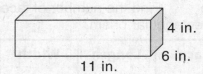

4 in.
6 in.
11 in.

_____

3. The puzzle that Jerry got for his birthday was in a box with a length of 15 in., a width of 8 in., and a height of 3 in. What is the surface area of the box?

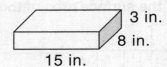

3 in.
8 in.
15 in.

_____

4. Jerry received another present that was 15 in. long, 7.5 in. wide, and 6 in. high. Is the surface area of this box greater than or less than the surface area of the box in Problem 3?

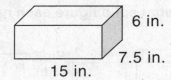

6 in.
7.5 in.
15 in.

_____

5. David stacked two boxes together as shown below. Each box measured 10 in. long, 5 in. high, and 3 in. wide. What is the exposed surface area of both boxes?

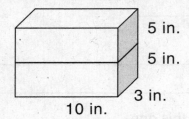

5 in.
5 in.
3 in.
10 in.

_____

6. Compare the surface area of Box A and Box B using >, <, or =.

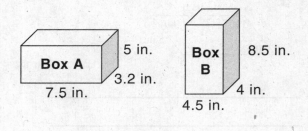

Box A
5 in.
3.2 in.
7.5 in.

Box B
8.5 in.
4 in.
4.5 in.

_____

Volume

CA Standard
KEY MG 1.3

Find the volume of the box.

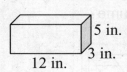

5 in.
3 in.
12 in.

$V = l \times w \times h$

$= 12 \text{ in.} \times 3 \text{ in.} \times 5 \text{ in.}$

$= 180 \text{ in}^3$

Solution: The volume is 180 in³.

Find the volume of each solid figure.

1.

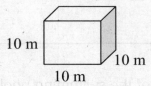

10 m
10 m
10 m

_____

2.

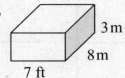

3 m
8 m
7 ft

_____

3.

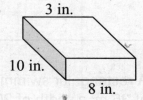

3 in.
10 in.
8 in.

_____

Spiral Review (Chapter 21, Lesson 2) **KEY** MG 1.1, MG 1.0

Find the area of each figure.

4.

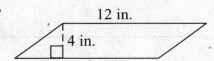

12 in.
4 in.

_____

5.

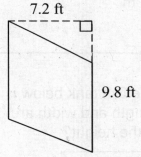

7.2 ft
9.8 ft

_____

6. Paul cut a rectangular piece of cardboard that measured 11 inches in length and 8 inches in width. What was the area of the piece of cardboard?

_____

Volume

CA Standard
KEY MG 1.3

Solve problems 1–6.

1. Paula built this figure out of blocks. What is the volume? **HINT:** Count the blocks to find the length, width, and height.

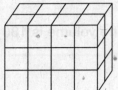

_____

2. Simon built the figure below using cubes. What is the volume?

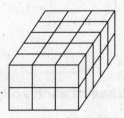

_____

3. A rectangular swimming pool has length of 35 m, a width of 20 m, and a depth of 6 m. What is the volume of the pool?

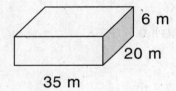

6 m
20 m
35 m

_____

4. Find the volume of the swimming pool below. What is the difference in volume between this swimming pool and the swimming pool from Problem 3?

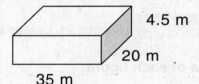

4.5 m
20 m
35 m

_____

5. The volume of the fish tank below is 2,880 in³. The length and width are labeled. What is the height?

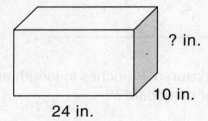

? in.
10 in.
24 in.

_____

6. Kevin's pencil box measured 28 cm in length, 20 cm in width, and 12 cm in height. Draw the pencil box. Then, find the volume.

Perimeter, Area, or Volume?

CA Standards
MR 2.4, MG 1.4

Solve. Tell whether you found perimeter, area, or volume.

Henry built a jewelry box for his mother using the pattern shown. How much fabric does he need to cover the top and sides?
Now he needs to use what he knows about surface area, volume, and perimeter to finish his present.

Henry needs to find the surface area without the bottom.

Remember, $A = l \cdot w$.
top face: 21 in.²
front and back faces: $2 \times (24.5 \text{ in.}^2) = 49 \text{ in.}^2$
side faces: $2 \times (10.5 \text{ in.}^2) = 21 \text{ in.}^2$
Solution: 21 in.² + 49 in.² + 21 in.² = 91 in.²

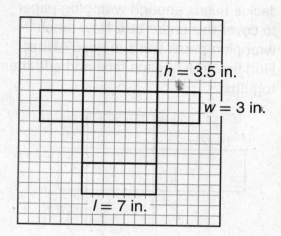

$h = 3.5$ in.
$w = 3$ in.
$l = 7$ in.

1. How much will the jewelry box hold?

_____

2. Henry wants to glue a photo of his family on the top face of the jewelry box. The photo has a length of 5 inches and a width of 3 inches. How much fabric is showing on the top face after the photo is glued on? HINT: Subtract the area of the photo from the area of the top face of the jewelry box.

_____

Spiral Review (Chapter 21, Lesson 2) **KEY MG 1.1, MG 1.0**

Find the area to solve.

3.

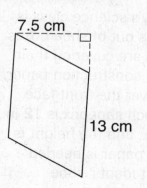

7.5 cm
13 cm

4.

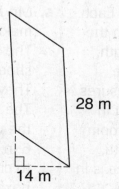

28 m
14 m

5. Jermaine drew this picture of his backyard. What is the area?

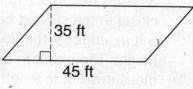

35 ft
45 ft

_____   _____   _____

Name _____ Date _____

Perimeter, Area, or Volume?

CA Standards
MR 2.4, MG 1.4

Solve. Tell whether you found perimeter, area, or volume.

1. Jackie needs enough wrapping paper to cover this entire box. How much wrapping paper will she need? **Hint:** Find the area of each face and add them together.

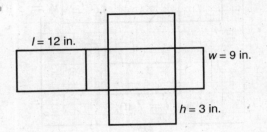

l = 12 in. *w* = 9 in. *h* = 3 in.

2. A cabinet stands 6 ft tall, 4 ft in length, and 2 ft in width. How many cubic feet of space is available in the cabinet? **Hint:** Volume = $L \times W \times H$

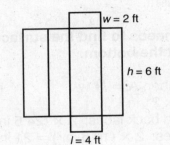

w = 2 ft *h* = 6 ft *l* = 4 ft

3. Abby bought a plastic storage container that measures 36 inches in length, 20 inches in width, and 24 inches in height. A strip of rubber was placed around the edges of the top of the container. How much rubber was used?

4. Rose's grandmother gave her a jewelry box for her birthday which is 18 cm long, 10 cm wide and 12.8 cm deep. Use the measurements of the jewelry box to find how many cubic cm are inside.

5. Mike's house has three bedrooms. Each bedroom has a closet. The closet in the first bedroom measures 5 ft in length, 3 ft in width, and 7 ft in height. The closet in the second bedroom measures 5 ft in length, 4 ft in width, and 7 ft in height. The closet in the third bedroom measures 5 ft in length, 8 ft in width, and 7 ft in height. How much space is in all three closets combined?

6. Mr. Montgomery's science class is making dioramas out of shoe boxes. The 24 students are covering their shoe boxes with construction paper. They can not cover the front face. The length of each shoebox is 12 in., the width is 8 in., and the height is 6 in. How much paper is needed to cover all 24 students' shoe boxes?

Hands On: Model Percent

CA Standards
KEY NS 1.2, MR 2.3

Write the percent of the grid that is shaded. Then write a decimal and a fraction in simplest form for the shaded part.

Step ① Write the percent shown by the shaded squares.

32% is shaded.

Step ② Write the percent as a decimal and a fraction.

$$32\% = 0.32$$
$$32\% = \frac{32}{100} = \frac{8}{25}$$

1.

_____

2.

_____

3.

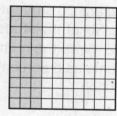

_____

4.

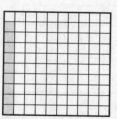

_____

5.

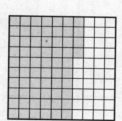

_____

6.

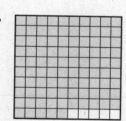

_____

Spiral Review (Chapter 1, Lesson 4) **NS 1.3, KEY NS 1.4**

Write using exponents. Then write the value of the expression.

7. $5 \times 5 \times 5 \times 5$ _____

8. 9×9 _____

9. The volume of a cube equals the length times the width times the height. Express the volume of a cube with side length 2 units using an exponent. Then write the value of the expression.

_____

Hands On: Model Percent

CA Standards
KEY NS 1.2, MR 2.3

Solve.

1. Tony shaded some of the squares on this hundreds grid. What fraction of squares did Tony shade? What percent of squares did Tony shade?

_____

_____

2. Marita spelled 84 out of 100 words correctly on her spelling test. Shade the hundreds grid below to show Marita's score. What percent of the words did Marita spell correctly?

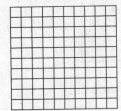

_____

3. There are 20 students in Jarrod's karate class. Six of the students are in third grade. Write the number of third grade students as a percent, a decimal, and as a fraction.

_____

4. Mrs. McCarthy asked George and Sarah to show 0.40 on hundreds grids. Who shaded their grid correctly?

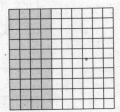 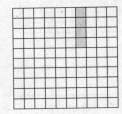

George   Sarah

_____

5. In the election for class president, Daphne received 40% of the votes, Felicia received 35% of the votes, and Chet received the rest of the votes. What percent did Chet receive?

_____

6. Roland bought a packet of sunflower seeds for his garden. On Saturday, he planted 65% of the seeds. How many seeds does Roland have left to plant? Write your answer as a percent, a decimal, and as a fraction.

_____

Relate Percents to Fractions and Decimals

CA Standards
KEY NS 1.2, MR 2.3

Write $\frac{4}{5}$ as a percent.

Way ① Use equivalent fractions. Write an equivalent fraction with a denominator of 100.

Think: 5 times what number equals 100?

$$\frac{4}{5} \overset{\times 20}{=} \frac{80}{100} \overset{\times 20}{}$$

Write the fraction as a percent.

$$\frac{80}{100} = 80\%$$

Solution: Both ways show that $\frac{4}{5}$ = 80%.

Way ② Use division.

Divide the numerator by the denominator.

$$\frac{4}{5} = 5\overline{)4.0}^{0.8}$$

Write the decimal as a percent.

0.8 = 0.80 = 80%

Find the percent by finding an equivalent fraction or dividing the numerator by the denominator.

1. $\frac{1}{20}$ _____

2. $\frac{3}{10}$ _____

3. $\frac{2}{5}$ _____

4. $\frac{7}{50}$ _____

5. $\frac{14}{20}$ _____

6. $\frac{15}{50}$ _____

7. $\frac{17}{20}$ _____

8. $\frac{23}{50}$ _____

9. $\frac{54}{100}$ _____

10. $\frac{11}{20}$ _____

11. $\frac{14}{25}$ _____

12. $\frac{3}{15}$ _____

Spiral Review (Chapter 1, Lesson 4) NS 1.3, **KEY** NS 1.4

Write using exponents. Then write the value of the expression.

13. $6 \times 6 \times 6 \times 6$ _____

14. $7 \times 7 \times 7 \times 7 \times 7 \times 7$ _____

15. Eight large boxes each contain 8 small boxes. Each small box weighs 8 ounces. Express the total weight of the small boxes using an exponent. Then evaluate.

_____

Relate Percents to Fractions and Decimals

CA Standards
KEY NS 1.2, MR 2.3

Solve.

1. At basketball camp, Cheryl was in a free throw competition. She attempted 10 shots and made 6 of them. What percent of free throws did Cheryl make? Write your answer as a percent and a decimal.

   $\frac{6}{10}$ = _____ % = _____

2. There were 45 students signed up for camp. Of those students, 18 were in third grade. What percent of students who signed up for camp were in third grade? Write your answer as a percent and as a decimal.
   (HINT: First, simplify the fraction. Then find the percent and decimal.)

   $\frac{18}{45}$ = _____ % = _____

3. The Houston Comets had the second-best record in the WNBA during the 2002 season. The Comets won 24 of their 32 games. What percent of their games did the Comets win?

   _____

4. Suppose that a basketball player attempted 20 three-point shots and made 5 of them. Write the number of shots that she made as a percent and as a decimal.

   _____

5. There are 25 students practicing soccer. Nine of the students are girls. What percent of the students are girls? What percent of the students are boys?

   _____

6. Tony made 85% of his field goal attempts. If he made 40 attempts, how many field goals did he make?

   _____

Compare and Order Fractions, Decimals, and Percents

CA Standards
KEY NS 1.2, MR 2.4

Compare $\frac{7}{10}$, 46%, and 0.63 to find the greatest.

Step 1 Rewrite the fraction as a decimal.	**Step 2** Think of the percent as a number of hundredths.	**Step 3** Compare.
$$\begin{array}{r} 0.7 \\ 10\overline{)7.0} \\ -7.0 \\ \hline 0 \end{array}$$	$46\% = \frac{46}{100} = 0.46$	$0.7 > 0.63 > 0.46$

Solution: $\frac{7}{10}$ is the greatest.

Which is greatest?

1. $\frac{3}{5}$ 0.56 55%

_____

2. $\frac{3}{8}$ 0.38 35%

_____

3. $\frac{2}{9}$ 0.25 24%

_____

4. $\frac{8}{11}$ 0.7 71%

_____

5. $\frac{6}{7}$ 0.4 86%

_____

6. $\frac{2}{3}$ 0.62 65%

_____

Which is least?

7. $\frac{1}{10}$ 0.11 19%

_____

8. $\frac{7}{10}$ 0.63 47%

_____

9. $\frac{3}{4}$ 0.71 73%

_____

Spiral Review (Chapter 21, Lesson 4) **MG 1.0, KEY MG 1.1**

Find the area of each figure.

10.

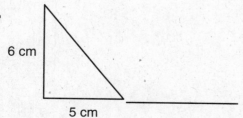

6 cm

5 cm

11.

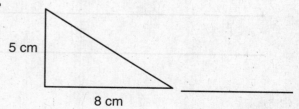

5 cm

8 cm

12. A triangular flag has a base of 20 inches and a height of 32 inches.

What is the area of the flag? _____

Compare and Order Fractions, Decimals, and Percents

Solve.

1. About 35% of the people who come to the park bring a dog. $\frac{2}{5}$ of people who come to the park exercise. Which group of people represents a larger percent of the people coming to the park?

   _____

2. Heavy rains fell on 52% of the country on Monday and $\frac{12}{25}$ of the country on Tuesday. On which day did a greater portion of the country receive rain?

   _____

3. In a survey of favorite ice cream, mint chocolate chip received 22% of the votes. Chocolate received $\frac{1}{4}$ of the votes and vanilla received 0.37 of the votes. Order the flavors from most to least popular

   _____

   _____

4. Mr. Davis's students were surveyed on their favorite subject. One fifth prefer math, 0.35 prefer social studies, and 45% prefer reading. Order the subjects from least favorite to most favorite.

   _____

   _____

5. Bart conducted a music survey among his friends. He reported that 0.42 prefer pop, 22% prefer rock, and $\frac{2}{5}$ prefer country. Explain what's wrong with Bart's results.

   _____

   _____

6. Forty percent of the students in Mrs. Henry's fourth grade class are 9 years old. Another 0.25 are 10 years old, and the rest of the class is 11 years old. Write the number of students that are 11 years old as a fraction, decimal, and percent.

   _____

Percent of a Number

CA Standards
KEY NS 1.2, MR 3.2

Find 25% of 60.

Way 1 Write the percent as a fraction.	**Way 2** Write the percent in decimal form.
$25\% = \frac{25}{100} = \frac{1}{4}$	$25\% = 0.25$
$\frac{1}{4} \times 60 = 15$	$0.25 \times 60 = 15$

Solution: 25% of 60 is 15.

Solve by writing the percent as a fraction.

1. 15% of 40 = n **2.** 90% of 30 = n **3.** 5% of 80 = n **4.** 75% of 20 = n

_____   _____   _____   _____

5. 12% of 25 = n **6.** 38% of 50 = n **7.** 40% of 25 = n **8.** 20% of 45 = n

_____   _____   _____   _____

Solve by writing the percent as a decimal.

9. 10% of 70 = n **10.** 14% of 50 = n **11.** 85% of 90 = n **12.** 29% of 55 = n

_____   _____   _____   _____

13. 30% of 61 = n **14.** 8% of 72 = n **15.** 2% of 57 = n **16.** 48% of 92 = n

_____   _____   _____   _____

Spiral Review (Chapter 22, Lesson 4) **KEY** MG 1.3

Find the volume of each solid figure.

17.

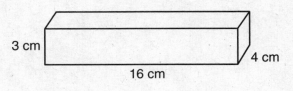

3 cm
16 cm
4 cm

18.

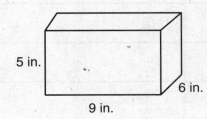

5 in.
9 in.
6 in.

_____   _____

19. A gift box is 13 inches long, 6 inches wide, and 3 inches high. What is the volume of the box?

_____

Percent of a Number

CA Standards
KEY NS 1.2, MR 3.2

Solve.

1. The cost of a large pizza was $20. Anna gave the delivery driver a 15% tip. What was the amount of the tip?

   _____

2. The bill for dinner was $76. Chuck left a 20% tip. How much was the tip?

   _____

3. Carol likes to leave 10% of one night's stay for the cleaning crew at a hotel. If the Highfield Hotel charges $155 per night, how much did Carol leave for the cleaning crew?

   _____

4. Which is greater, 20% of 40 or 40% of 20? Explain your answer.

   _____

   _____

5. Deanna said she can find 60% of a number by finding 10% of a number and multiplying by 6. Is Deanna correct? Give an example.

   _____

   _____

   _____

   _____

6. The cost of dinner for a family of four was $128. They left the waiter a total of $151.04, including the tip. What percent of the bill was the tip?

   _____

Problem Solving: Percent Problems

CA Standards
KEY NS 1.2, MR 2.6

Example 1 Sometimes you want to find the percent of a number.

The pool where Jeremy swims is 40 feet long. For 60% of that length, the water is shallow. For what length of the pool is the water shallow?

What number is 60% of 40?

$n = 0.60 \times 40$ $\qquad$ $n = 24$ feet

Example 2 Sometimes you want to find what percent one number is of another number.

Jeremy wants to swim 15 lengths of the pool. He has completed 3.75 lengths. What percent has he completed?

What percent of 15 is 3.75?

$15 \times n = 3.75$ $\qquad$ $n = \dfrac{3.75}{15}$

$n = 0.25 = 25\%$

Example 3 Sometimes you want to find a number when a percent is known.

The pool is in a building 60 feet wide. That is 75% of the length of the building. How long is the building?

75% of what number equals 60?

$0.75 \times n = 60$ $\qquad$ $n = \dfrac{60}{0.75}$ $\qquad$ $n = 80$ feet

Solve.

1. Out of 40 newspapers that Maureen sells at her news stand, 85% are copies of the Small Town Journal. How many copies of the Small Town Journal does she sell?

   _____

2. David's class voted on what kind of cookies to have for the party. Out of a class of 20 students, 12 voted for chocolate chip. What percent voted for chocolate chip?

   _____

Spiral Review (Chapter 22, Lesson 3) **KEY** MG 1.3, MG 1.4

Find the volume of each solid figure.

3.
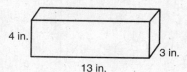
4 in.
3 in.
13 in.

4.
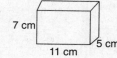
7 cm
11 cm
5 cm

_____ $\qquad\qquad$ _____

5. Tracy's sandbox has a length of 4 feet, a width of 2 feet, and a height of 1 foot. What is the volume of her sandbox? _____

Problem Solving: Percent Problems

CA Standards
KEY NS 1.2, MR 2.6

Solve.

1. Noah spent 50 minutes cleaning his room. For 20% of that time, he put away clothes. How long did he put away clothes? Hint: Write 20% as 0.20, then multiply by 50.

   _____

2. Out of 80 members of the community recreation club, 60 voted to have a spaghetti dinner each month. What percent voted to have a spaghetti dinner each month? Hint: Start by writing "60 out of 80" as $\frac{60}{80}$.

   _____

3. Ten of the students in Kelly's class take dance classes after school. That number is 40% of the students in the class. How many students are in Kelly's class?

   _____

4. In Colin's school there are 300 students. If 138 are boys, what percent are girls?

   _____

5. At Harry's Secondhand Shop, clothing is priced at 45% of the price it would be if it were new. Sales tax of 5% is added to each purchase. What would the final cost be for a shirt that was priced at $24 when it was new?

   _____

6. Tori bought her skates at a clearance sale. The clearance price was 25% off the first sale price. The first sale price was 15% off the original price. If the clearance price was $51, what were the sale and original prices? Hint: If a new price is 25% off, what percent of the old price is it?

   _____

Hands On: Make a Circle Graph

CA Standard
KEY NS 1.2, SDAP 1.2

Use Circle Graphs.

Jenna asked students to name an activity they do after school. She displayed her results in a table. Make a circle graph to display the data.

After School Activities	
watching television	45%
riding bikes	15%
playing video games	25%
reading a book	15%

Step 1 Use the percents to find the number of degrees needed to draw each section of the circle graph.

$0.45 \times 360° = 162°$

$0.15 \times 360° = 54°$

$0.25 \times 360° = 90°$

$0.15 \times 360° = 54°$

Step 2 Use a compass to draw a circle. Use a protractor to measure and draw each section of the graph.

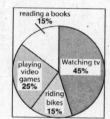

Use the circle graph for Problems 1 and 2.

1. If 300 students were surveyed, how many students ride bikes after school? _____

2. How many more students play video games than read a book after school? _____

3. How many students watch tv or ride bikes? _____

Spiral Review (Chapter 16, Lesson 5) **AF 1.1, SDAP 1.2**

Use the histogram to answer the questions.

4. How many students are between 53–56 inches in height? _____

5. How many students are at least 57 inches or taller? _____

6. A new student enters the fifth grade. His height is 62 inches. How does this students' height change the histogram?

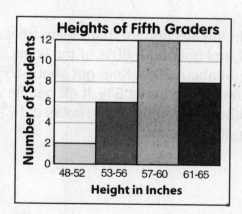

_____

_____

Make a Circle Graph

CA Standards
KEY NS 1.2, SDAP 1.2

Solve.

1. The circle graph shows percents of customers who buy cookies, cakes, and pies at Betty's Cookie Bakery. Did more customers buy cakes or pies?

Betty's Cookie Bakery

Pies 15% — Cakes 20% — Cookies 65%

_____

2. Last week, Betty had a total of 500 customers. Use the percents in the circle graph to tell how many customers bought cookies.
Hint: Find 65% of 500.

_____

3. Sam surveyed his friends and found that 75% of them liked to wear jeans to school, 15% liked to wear cargo pants, and 10% liked to wear dresses. If he surveyed 20 people, how many liked to wear cargo pants?

_____

4. If you were going to make a circle graph for the percents in Problem 3, what would the number of degrees be for each section?

_____

5. In the election for math team treasurer, Carol got about 60% of the votes, Jose got about 20%, Kate got about 15%, and James got about 5%. If 42 people voted, about how many more votes did Carol get than James?

_____

6. The math team also voted for a mascot. Of the 42 voters, 16 wanted a bulldog, 12 wanted a bobcat, 8 wanted a polar bear, 5 wanted a raccoon, and 1 wanted a hamster. About what percent wanted each mascot? Round to the nearest percent.

_____

Name _____ Date _____

Compare Data Sets

CA Standards
SDAP 1.3, **KEY** NS 1.2

Ed has 45 baseball cards. Twelve of them are rookie cards. Steve has 28 baseball cards. Twelve of them are rookie cards. Whose collection has a greater percent of rookie cards?

Write the parts as fractions in simplest form.

$$\frac{12}{45} = \frac{4}{15} \qquad \frac{12}{28} = \frac{3}{7}$$

Way ❶ Compare fractions. You can compare by using a common denominator.

$$\frac{4}{15} = \frac{28}{105} \qquad \frac{3}{7} = \frac{45}{105} \qquad \frac{28}{105} < \frac{45}{105} \qquad \text{so} \qquad \frac{12}{45} < \frac{12}{28}$$

Way ❷ Compare percents. Express each fraction as a percent, and then compare.

$$\frac{4}{15} = 27\% \qquad \frac{3}{7} = 43\% \qquad 27\% < 43\% \qquad \text{so} \qquad \frac{12}{45} < \frac{12}{28}$$

Solution: Steve has a greater percent of rookie cards.

**Write each set as a fraction in simplest form and as a percent.
Then order the percents from least to greatest.**

1. 6 out of 10 _____

2. 4 out of 20 _____

3. 5 out of 50 _____

4. 6 out of 15 _____

Compare. Use >, <, or = for each ◯ _____

5. 5 out of 25 ◯ 12 out of 48 _____

6. 18 out of 30 ◯ 10 out of 25

7. 3 out of 12 ◯ 12 out of 48

8. 30 out of 40 ◯ 16 out of 20

Spiral Review (Chapter 16, Lesson 5) **AF 1.1, SDAP 1.2**

Use the line graph to answer questions 9–11.

9. How many more chickadees than nuthatches did Joey see

   on the birdfeeder on Tuesday? _____

10. On which day was the number of chickadees closest to

    the number of nuthatches? _____

11. On Saturday, Joey counted 3 times as many nuthatches and half as many chickadees as

    on Thursday. How many of each bird did he count on Saturday? _____

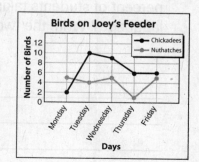

Birds on Joey's Feeder

Name _____ Date _____

Compare Data Sets

Solve.

1. Ferris bought 12 apples and 10 oranges at the market. He gave 4 apples and 2 oranges to his friend. Did he give away a higher percent of apples or oranges? Use fractions to solve the problem.

$\frac{4}{12} =$ _____

$\frac{2}{10} =$ _____

_____

_____

_____

2. Kathy has 100 songs on her music player. 40 of them are by solo singers. Beth has 200 songs on her music player, and 60 of them are by solo singers. Who has the higher percent of songs by solo singers? Use percents to solve the problem.

$\frac{40}{100} = \frac{2}{5}$

$\frac{60}{200} = \frac{3}{10}$

_____

_____

_____

3. The library where Jason borrows movies has 100 DVDs in its collection. 25 are cartoons. The library also has 80 videos, of which 24 are cartoons. Which has a higher percent of cartoons: the DVD collection or the video collection?

_____

4. Jason has 25 DVDs and 16 videos at home. Of these, 5 DVDs and 4 videos are action films. Does he have a higher percent of action DVDs or action videos?

_____

5. At Central Middle School, there are 656 students. 492 of them take a foreign language. At Eastern Middle School, there are 480 students. 384 take a foreign language. Which school has a higher percent of students taking a foreign language? Write the two percents.

_____

_____

_____

6. Chloe took a pottery class for a year. Altogether, she and her classmates made 144 bowls and 96 vases in the first six months. In the second six months, they made 117 bowls and 63 vases. In which part of the year did they make a higher percent of bowls? Write percents for bowls and vases for each part of the year.

_____

_____

_____

Mental Math: Percent of a Number

CA Standards
KEY NS 1.2, NS 1.0

Find 10% of 75

Way **1** Multiply by $\frac{1}{10}$.

$$\frac{1}{10} \times \frac{75}{1} = \frac{75}{10}$$
$$= 7.5$$

Way **2** Move the decimal point one place to the left to divide by 10.

$$75 \div 10 = 7.5$$

Use mental math to find each number.

1. 10% of 167 _____

2. 75% of 12 _____

3. 25% of 160 _____

4. 50% of 62 _____

5. 20% of 80 _____

6. 75% of 32 _____

7. 20% of 20 _____

8. 10% of 175 _____

Spiral Review   (Chapter 17, Lessons 3 and 4) **KEY** SDAP 1.5, **KEY** AF 1.5

Copy and complete the function tables.

9.

$y = 3x$	
x	**y**
	3
	9
$\frac{1}{2}$	
8	

10.

$y = x - 2$	
x	**y**
	12
7	
	4
$5\frac{1}{2}$	

11. Janet was going to a concert for her birthday. She planned to bring at least one friend, and pay for all the tickets. Each ticket costs $5, and she also had to pay $3 to park the car. Complete the function table to find the cost for Janet and one or more of her friends.

$y = 5x + 3$	
x	**y**
2	
	$18
4	
	$28

Use with text pp. 526–527

Name _____ Date _____

Mental Math: Percent of a Number

CA Standards
KEY NS 1.2, NS 1.0

Solve.

1. Carolyn's family had a family reunion. In all, 50 family members attended. Of those who attended, 10% were grandparents. How many grandparents were at the family reunion?

   $\frac{1}{10} \times \frac{50}{1} =$

   _____

2. Mikko's new organizer has 150 pages. 20% of the pages are blank sheets for notes. How many pages are blank? Hint: Find 10% then multiply by 2 to find 20%.

   _____

3. Edmund is painting his living room walls. The smallest wall measures 64 square feet. He can paint 75% of this wall with one small can of paint. Use mental math to determine how many square feet he can paint with one can of paint.

   _____

4. A family of four had dinner at their favorite Mexican restaurant. The cost of the dinner was $78. If the family plans to leave a 20% tip, how much tip will the waiter receive?

   _____

5. Audrey's school put on a fun fair to raise money for charity. Audrey's job was to calculate donations based on tickets sold. The tickets to the fair were $3 each, and 275 people attended. If the school was giving 15% of the ticket sales to charity, how much money were they able to give?

   _____

6. Zander was in charge of calculating profit at the refreshments booth. The booth offered lemonade at 50 cents a glass, cookies at 3 for $1.00, and popcorn at 75 cents a bag. They sold 175 glasses of lemonade, 300 cookies, and 150 bags of popcorn. Of the money they received, 55% went toward paying for ingredients, leaving the remainder for profit. How much profit did they make on refreshments?

   _____

Name _____ Date _____

Hands On: Positive and Negative Numbers

CA Standard
KEY NS 1.5

Use a number line to find the distance between ⁻6 and 0.
What is the absolute value of ⁻6?

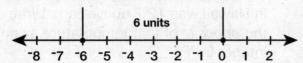

6 units

⁻8 ⁻7 ⁻6 ⁻5 ⁻4 ⁻3 ⁻2 ⁻1 0 1 2

⁻6 is 6 units from zero.

Solution: The absolute value of ⁻6 is 6.

Write the opposite of each number.

1. ⁻12   **2.** ⁻5   **3.** ⁺18   **4.** ⁺29

_____   _____   _____   _____

5. ⁺73   **6.** ⁻92   **7.** ⁻317   **8.** ⁺47

_____   _____   _____   _____

Write the absolute value for each number.

9. 0   **10.** ⁻16   **11.** ⁺77   **12.** ⁻4

_____   _____   _____   _____

13. ⁺9   **14.** ⁻15   **15.** ⁺22   **16.** ⁻11

_____   _____   _____   _____

Spiral Review   (Chapter 24, Lesson 3) **KEY** NS 1.2, NS 1.0

Use mental math to find each number.

17. 25% of 400 _____

18. 10% of 315 _____

19. Mary and three friends went to lunch. Their total bill was $28. If they
want to leave a 20% tip, how much tip will the waiter receive?

_____

Hands On: Positive and Negative Numbers

CA Standard
KEY NS 1.5

Solve.

1. The lowest temperature ever recorded in Alaska was 80°F below zero. Write that temperature as an integer in °F .
(Hint: Below zero indicates a negative number)

_____

2. The lowest temperature ever recorded in Hawaii was 12°F above zero. Write the *opposite* of that temperature as an integer in °F.

_____

3. In football, teams can gain or lose yards. In one play, a quarterback lost 8 yards. Write that loss as an integer, then write its opposite.

_____

4. Professional golfers try to score under par, which is the average number of strokes needed for each hole. Draw a number line with par marked at the zero point. Record these three scores as positive or negative integers on the number line: 4 under par, 3 over par, 1 under par.

_____

_____

5. The coldest temperature ever recorded on earth was ⁻129°F. The highest temperature ever recorded was 136°F. What is the difference of the two temperatures?

_____

6. The highest temperature ever recorded in the United States was 134°F in California. The lowest temperature ever recorded was ⁻80°F in Alaska. Explain how to find the difference of the two temperatures. Write the difference.

_____

_____

_____

_____

Compare and Order Integers

CA Standard
KEY NS 1.5

Order 1, ⁻2 and ⁻3 from least to greatest.

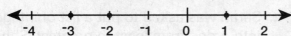

⁻4 ⁻3 ⁻2 ⁻1 0 1 2

The integer farthest to the left is the least, and the integer farthest to the right is the greatest.

⁻3 < ⁻2 < ⁺1

Solution: The numbers in order from least to greatest are ⁻3, ⁻2, ⁺1.

Compare. Draw a number line from ⁻8 to ⁺8 and label each integer.
Write >, <, or = for each ⬭.

1. ⁺3 ⬭ 0   **2.** ⁻1 ⬭ ⁻4   **3.** ⁻5 ⬭ ⁻1   **4.** ⁻2 ⬭ 0

5. ⁺1 ⬭ ⁺4   **6.** ⁻5 ⬭ ⁻2   **7.** ⁻1 ⬭ ⁻7   **8.** ⁺4 ⬭ ⁻3

Write the integers in order from least to greatest. Draw a number line if you wish.

9. ⁻4, ⁻7, ⁻3, 0

_____

10. ⁺3, ⁻5, ⁺2, ⁻1

_____

11. ⁻12, ⁺8, ⁻9, ⁺10

_____

12. ⁺1, ⁻3, ⁻2, ⁺2

_____

Spiral Review (Chapter 24, Lesson 3) **KEY** NS 1.2, NS 1.0

Use mental math to find each number.

13. 100% of 97 _____

14. 25% of 236 _____

15. Jacob is reading a book that has 160 pages. So far he has read 75% of the book. How many pages has he read?

_____

Name _____   Date _____

Compare and Order Integers

CA Standard
KEY NS 1.5

Solve.

1. Put this list of integers in order, from least to greatest: $^-1, ^+2, ^+5, ^-3, ^+1$. Some are done for you.

   _____, $^-1$, _____, $^+2$, _____

2. Sarah was asked to put a list of integers into order, from least to greatest. She wrote the numbers in this order: $^+2, ^-3, ^+4, ^-5, ^+5$. What did she do wrong? What is the correct order?

   _____

   _____

   _____

3. In golf, the lowest score wins. Five golfers scored $^-3, ^+5, ^-4, ^+2,$ and $^+3$. Order the score from the best score to the worst score.

   _____

4. Write two numbers that are better than the worst score in Problem 2 but not as good as the middle score.

   _____

   _____

5. Put this set of numbers in order, from least to greatest: $^+3, ^-5, ^+4, ^-9, ^-2, ^+7, ^-1, ^+6$. Which number has the greatest absolute value?

   _____

   _____

   _____

6. If you take 25% of a negative integer, will the new number be greater or less than the original integer? Explain and give an example.

   _____

   _____

   _____

   _____

   _____

   _____

   _____

Name _____ Date _____

Add Integers

CA Standard
KEY NS 2.1

Find ⁻4 + ⁺5.

Step 1 Use circles to show negative integers.

Step 2 Use squares to show positive integers.

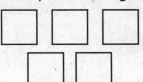

Step 3 Match each circle to a square.

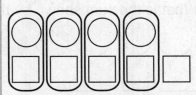

Since 1 square remains, the sum is positive 1.

Solution: ⁻4 + ⁺5 = ⁺1

Write the addition expression shown by the circles and squares and then find the sum.

1. ☐☐☐◯ _____

2. ◯◯◯◯◯☐☐ _____

3. ◯◯◯◯☐☐☐ _____

4. ☐☐☐☐◯◯◯ _____

Solve. Use counters to help you.

5. ⁺8 + ⁻6 _____

6. ⁻7 + ⁻5 _____

7. ⁻7 + ⁺2 _____

8. ⁻9 + ⁺8 _____

9. ⁺6 + ⁻10 _____

10. ⁻11 + ⁺6 _____

11. ⁻3 + ⁻2 _____

12. ⁺10 + ⁻3 _____

Spiral Review (Chapter 24, Lesson 3) **KEY** NS 1.2, NS 1.0

Use mental math to find each number.

13. 25% of 452 _____

14. 20% of 300 _____

15. Sara bought a sweater on sale for 10% off the original price. If the sweater was originally $32, how much money did she save?

_____

Add Integers

CA Standard
KEY NS 2.1

Solve. White counters are positive. Gray counters are negative.

1. Kelly used counters to make this model but needs help completing the expression. Find the missing integers. What is the sum shown by the counters?

___ + $^-3$ = ___

2. Jamie wrote the expression $^+2 + {}^-4 = {}^+2$ to represent this model. What mistake did Jamie make? Write the correct expression.

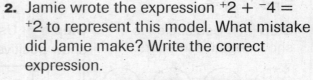

_____

_____

_____

3. Sarah made the model below to represent $^+1 + {}^-5$. What is the sum?

_____

4. How many counters will Rebecca use to model the sum of the expression $^-3 + {}^+5$?

_____

5. Adam and Joe both made models of the expression $^-3 + {}^+2 + {}^-2$. Whose model is correct? Explain.

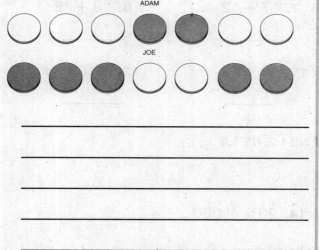

_____

_____

_____

_____

_____

_____

6. Mrs. Jessen asked her class to write the equation shown by this model. What is the equation shown?

_____

Add Integers On a Number Line

CA Standards
KEY NS 2.1, KEY NS 1.5

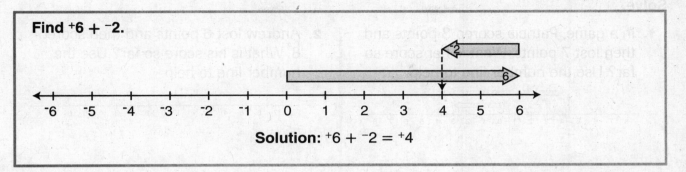

Find $^+6 + {}^-2$.

Solution: $^+6 + {}^-2 = {}^+4$

Use a number line to add.

1. $^-2 + {}^+5$ 2. $^-8 + {}^+7$ 3. $^-6 + {}^-3$ 4. $^+8 + {}^+6$

_____   _____   _____   _____

5. $^-1 + {}^-9$ 6. $^-8 + {}^+10$ 7. $^+11 + {}^-9$ 8. $^-10 + {}^+7$

_____   _____   _____   _____

Find each sum. Then compare. Write >, <, or =.

9. $^-2 + {}^+5$ ◯ $^+3 + {}^-1$ 10. $^-3 + {}^-2$ ◯ $^-7 + {}^+2$

11. $^-1 + {}^+1$ ◯ $^-1 + {}^-1$ 12. $^-7 + {}^-2$ ◯ $^-3 + {}^-4$

Spiral Review (Chapter 24, Lesson 3) **KEY NS 1.2, NS 1.0**

Use mental math to find each number.

13. 10% of 815 _____   14. 20% of 500 _____

15. During the election for class president Marie received 25% of the vote and Rachel received 50% of the vote. If 60 people voted, how many more votes did Rachel receive than Marie?

_____

Homework

229

Use with text pp. 550–552

Add Integers on a Number Line

CA Standards
KEY NS 2.1, **KEY** NS 1.5

Solve.

1. In a game, Patricia scored 3 points and then lost 7 points. What is her score so far? Use the number line to help.

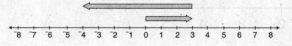

⁻8 ⁻7 ⁻6 ⁻5 ⁻4 ⁻3 ⁻2 ⁻1 0 1 2 3 4 5 6 7 8

_____

2. Andrew lost 6 points and then scored 8. What is his score so far? Use the number line to help.

⁻8 ⁻7 ⁻6 ⁻5 ⁻4 ⁻3 ⁻2 ⁻1 0 1 2 3 4 5 6 7 8

_____

3. Josh had 4 points. He lost twice as many points. Then he scored 10 points. How many points did he have in all? Mark each step of his point scores and losses on a number line.

⁻6 ⁻5 ⁻4 ⁻3 ⁻2 ⁻1 0 1 2 3 4 5 6

_____

4. Susan scored 6 points, lost 5 points, scored 2 points, and lost 4 points. How many points does she need to score to have zero points? Mark each step of her point scores and losses on a number line.

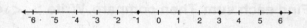

⁻6 ⁻5 ⁻4 ⁻3 ⁻2 ⁻1 0 1 2 3 4 5 6

_____

5. In the second quarter of the football game, Robin ran 14 yards in his first play. In his second play he ran 12 yards, but in his third play he lost 10 yards. How many yards did Robin gain after the three plays?

_____

6. Derek started at the 15 yard line on his team's side of the field. He ran for 12 yards before he got tackled. During the next play, Derek lost 7 yards. What yard did Derek reach after his two plays?

_____

Hands On: Subtract Integers

CA Standard
KEY NS 2.1

Find ⁻3 − ⁺1.

Step 1 Use circles to show negative integers. Use squares to show positive integers.

Step 2 You need to subtract ⁺1 but there are no squares to take away. Add a circle and a square to show 0.

Step 3 Take away a square to subtract ⁺1. What is left?

Since 4 circles remain, the difference is negative 4.
Solution: ⁻3 − ⁺1 = ⁻4

Write a subtraction expression. Then find the difference.

1.

Take away 2 squares.

_____

2.

Take away 7 circles.

_____

Use two-color counters to find each difference.

3. ⁺1 − ⁻5   4. ⁻2 − ⁺3   5. ⁻6 − ⁻1   6. ⁺2 − ⁻2

_____   _____   _____   _____

7. ⁺9 − ⁻11   8. ⁻7 − ⁻5   9. ⁺8 − ⁻5   10. ⁺8 − ⁻1

_____   _____   _____   _____

Spiral Review   (Chapter 23, Lesson 2) **KEY NS 1.2**

Find the percent by finding an equivalent fraction or dividing the numerator by the denominator.

11. $\frac{6}{20}$ _____

12. $\frac{3}{8}$ _____

13. In a survey 8 out of 20 people chose pepperoni as their favorite pizza. What percent of those surveyed chose pepperoni?

_____

Subtract Integers

CA Standard
KEY NS 2.1

Solve. White counters are positive. Black counters are negative.

1. Martin subtracted ⁻3 from ⁻5. what was his answer?

$$^-5 - {}^-3 = \underline{\hspace{1cm}}$$

2. What is the difference when you subtract ⁺3 from ⁺2?

$$^+2 - {}^+3 = \underline{\hspace{1cm}}$$

3. Carlos and his friends are playing a trivia game. For each correct answer, a player adds 1 point. For each incorrect answer a player subtracts 1 point. Carlos's score is ⁺3. What would be Carlos's score if he answers the next 5 questions incorrectly? Write an equation and solve.

_____

4. Eileen wrote that ⁻4 − ⁺4 = 0. Explain what Eileen's mistake was. Then tell the correct answer.

_____

_____

_____

5. The sum of two integers is ⁻3. The difference of the same two integers is ⁻13. What are the integers?

_____

_____

6. If a negative integer is subtracted from a positive integer, can the answer be 0? Explain and give an example.

_____

_____

_____

_____

_____

_____

_____

Subtract Integers On a Number Line

CA Standards
KEY NS 1.5, **KEY** NS 2.1

Use a number line to find ⁻2 − ⁻8.

Step 1 Start at 0. Model the first number by moving left 2 units to ⁻2.

Step 2 To subtract ⁻8, move 8 units to the right.

Step 3 The number you stop on is the answer.

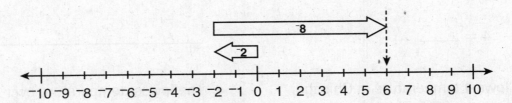

Solution: ⁻2 − ⁻8 = ⁺6

Use the number line to subtract.

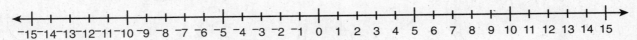

1. 0 − ⁻6

2. ⁻3 − ⁻11

3. ⁻9 − ⁻1

4. ⁺6 − ⁻4

_____

_____

_____

_____

5. ⁻11 − ⁺4

6. ⁻12 − ⁻8

7. ⁺3 − ⁻6

8. ⁺4 − ⁺7

_____

_____

_____

_____

9. ⁺6 − ⁺9

10. ⁻12 − ⁻5

11. ⁻5 − 0

12. ⁺8 − ⁻2

_____

_____

_____

_____

Spiral Review (Chapter 23, Lesson 2) **KEY** NS 1.2

Find the percent by finding an equivalent fraction or dividing the numerator by the denominator.

13. $\frac{2}{5}$ _____

14. $\frac{5}{20}$ _____

15. The Ice Cream Shoppe took a survey of 60 customers. Fifteen customers said strawberry was their favorite flavor of ice cream. Write $\frac{15}{60}$ as a percent.

_____

Subtract Integers on a Number Line

Solve.

1. What is the difference when you subtract
⁻4 from ⁻3?

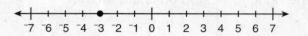

⁻3 − ⁻4 = _____

2. The temperature in the afternoon
was 12°F. The temperature dropped
15 degrees by the evening. What was
the temperature in the evening?
Hint: Subtract ⁺12 − ⁺15.

_____

3. The lowest temperature in Chicago,
Illinois was ⁻27°F. The lowest
temperature in Portland, Maine, was
⁻39°F. What is the difference between
the two lowest temperatures? Write an
equation and solve.

_____

4. The lowest temperature ever recorded
in Florida was ⁻2°F. If you subtract 43°F,
you will find the lowest temperature
ever recorded in California. What is that
temperature?

_____

5. As a science experiment, the class
placed three thermometers in different
locations. Thermometer A recorded a
temperature of 6°C. Thermometer B
recorded a temperature 9 degrees less
than Thermometer A. Thermometer
C recorded a temperature 3 degrees
warmer than Thermometer B. What were
the three temperature readings?

_____

_____

_____

6. Can you subtract two positive numbers
and get a negative number? Explain and
give an example.

_____

_____

_____

_____

_____

_____

_____

Add and Subtract Integers

CA Standard
KEY NS 2.1

Rules for Adding and Subtracting Integers

- You can turn any subtraction expression into addition by adding the opposite.
- The sum of two positive integers is positive.
- The sum of two negative integers is negative.
- The sum of a positive integer and a negative integer will have the same sign as the integer with the greater absolute value.

Decide if the sum or difference is positive or negative. Explain how you decided. Then solve.

1. $^-6 + {}^-8$

_____

2. $^-7 + {}^+10$

_____

_____

3. $^+1 + {}^-5$

_____

_____

4. $^-10 - {}^-4$

_____

_____

_____

_____

Spiral Review (Chapter 25, Lesson 2) **KEY NS 1.5**

Compare. Write >, <, or = for the ◯ **.**

5. $^-6$ ◯ $^+2$ **6.** $^-3$ ◯ $^-5$

7. Put this set of numbers in order, from least to greatest: $^+5$, $^-2$, $^+1$, $^-3$.

_____

Add and Subtract Integers

CA Standard
KEY NS 2.1

Solve problems 1–6.

1. Becky owes her mom $7. She pays back $5. Does Becky still owe her mom money? If so, how much?

2. Richard scored ⁺3 points and then he lost 5 points. What is his total score? Write a number sentence and solve.

3. The temperature on Tuesday morning was ⁺4°F. The temperature on Wednesday morning was ⁻6°F. What is the change in temperature from Tuesday to Wednesday morning? Write a number sentence and solve.

4. Janie borrowed $12 from Nick. Last week, Janie loaned Nick $7. Who owes whom money, and how much?

5. Gina had one ten–dollar bill and four one–dollar bills. She spent $7 on a book and $2 on a pen. Then she found one one–dollar bill in her coat pocket. How much money does Gina have now?

6. Eddie subtracted these three integers in some order.
⁻5 ⁺2 ⁺3
His answer was ⁺4. Is this possible? Explain.

Problem Solving: Use a Number Line

CA Standards
KEY NS 1.5, MR 2.3

The temperature rose from −7°F in the morning to 5°F by afternoon. How much did the temperature increase?

Understand.
Morning temperature: −7°F   Afternoon temperature: 5°F

Plan.
Use a number line.

Solve.

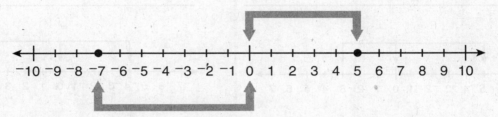

Solution: The total change in temperature: 12°F

Look Back.
Did you answer the question that was asked?
The temperature increased by 12°F.

Use a number line to solve. Explain why your answer makes sense.

1. The temperature was reported as 6°F. With the wind chill, the temperature felt as if it were ⁻6°F. What was the difference in temperature due to the wind chill?

_____

2. The temperature of a snow cone increased from ⁻10°F to 12°F. How much did the temperature increase?

_____

Spiral Review   (Chapter 25, Lesson 2) **KEY** NS 1.5

Compare. Write >, <, or =.

3. ⁻8 ◯ 2

4. ⁻3 ◯ 0

5. On the first down in a football game, a running back ran 12 yards. On the next down, he lost 7 yards. During which down did the running back run the greater distance?

_____

Problem Solving: Use a Number Line

Use a number line to solve. Explain why your answer makes sense.

1. The temperature rose from ⁻5°F to 3°F. What was the increase in temperature in degrees Fahrenheit?

2. The thermometer read 5°F. Due to the wind chill, the temperature felt as if it were ⁻4°F. What was the difference in temperature?

_____

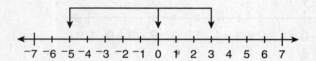

_____

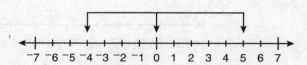

3. At 6:00 A.M., the temperature was ⁻4°F. By 2:00 P.M., the temperature had risen by 16°F. What was the temperature at 2:00 P.M.?

4. The thermometer read ⁻3°F in the freezer and 35°F in the refrigerator. What was the difference in temperature between the freezer and refrigerator?

_____

5. On Thursday, the temperature rose from ⁻15°F to ⁻2°F. On Friday, the temperature rose from ⁻7°F to 7°F. Which day had a greater increase in temperature?

6. The weather report predicted the average weekly temperature to be 28°F. A fifth grade class recorded the weekly temperatures as 12°F on Monday, 18°F on Tuesday, 25°F on Wednesday, 30°F on Thursday, and 35°F on Friday. Find the difference between the predicted average temperature and the actual average temperature.

_____

_____

Hands On:
Plot Points in the Coordinate Plane

CA Standard
KEY AF 1.4, **KEY** SDAP 1.5

- A coordinate plane is formed by two perpendicular lines called axes that lie in the plane.
- The horizontal axis is called the *x*-axis, and the vertical axis is called the *y*-axis.
- The axes divide the grid into 4 quadrants, numbered I, II, III, and IV.
- Every point on a coordinate plane is named by an ordered pair, (*x*, *y*).
- The point named by the ordered pair (0, 0) is the origin.

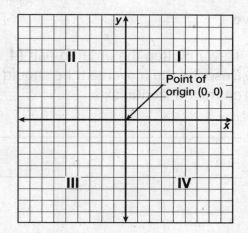

Use the graph for Problems 1–12. Write the ordered pair for each point.

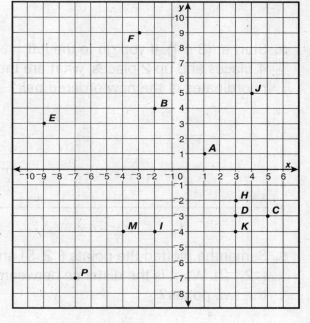

1. *I* _____

2. *A* _____

3. *C* _____

4. *B* _____

5. *P* _____

6. *H* _____

Write the letter name for each point.

7. (⁻9, ⁺3) _____

8. (⁺4, ⁺5) _____

9. (⁺3, ⁻4) _____

10. (⁻4, ⁻4) _____

11. (⁻3, ⁺9) _____

12. (3, ⁻3) _____

Spiral Review (Chapter 23, Lesson 4) **KEY NS 1.2, MR 3.2**

Find the value of *x*.

13. *x* = 25% of 100 = _____

14. 33% of 30 = *x* _____

15. Juan saw a pair of sneakers on sale for 20% off. If the price of the sneakers is $60, how much will Juan save?

_____

Hands On:
Plot Points in the Coordinate Plane

CA Standards
KEY AF 1.4, **KEY** SDAP 1.5

Solve.

1. Trevor plotted the ordered pair (4, ⁻6). Describe the movement he should make on the horizontal axis.

_____

_____

2. Plot the letter A on the coordinate grid at (2, 5).

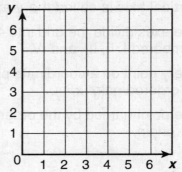

_____

3. Start at (3, ⁻4). If you go to the left 4 places and up 2 places, what are the coordinates of the new ordered pair?

_____

_____

4. India plotted the ordered pairs (1, 3), (3, 3) and (3, 1). She connected the points and said she made a square. Explain what India's mistake was. How could she correct her mistake?

_____

_____

5. Samantha plotted the points (⁻2, 5) and (⁻2, ⁻2). What is the distance between the two points?

_____

_____

6. Natalie plotted the ordered pairs (4, ⁻1), (1, ⁻4), (10, ⁻7), and (7, 2). If she connects the points, what figure does she make?

_____

_____

Read a Map

CA Standards
KEY AF 1.4, **KEY** SDAP 1.4

- Ordered pairs can be used to locate points on a map.
- Use a compass to identify the directions of North, South, East, and West.

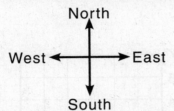

North

West ⟵⟶ East

South

- Plot the ordered pairs on the coordinate grid.
- Find the distance between two points by counting the number of units.

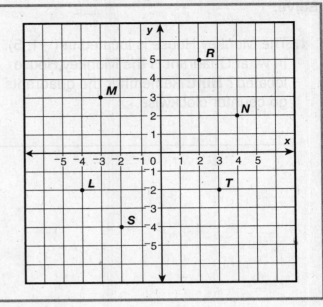

Use the map. Write the location for the letter.

1. R _____

2. S _____

3. T _____

4. L _____

5. M _____

6. N _____

Use the map below. Write the letter that you can see at each location.

7. (4, −3) _____

8. (−2, 4) _____

9. (2, 2) _____

10. (−5, −3) _____

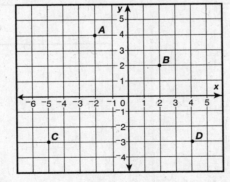

Spiral Review (Chapter 23, Lesson 4) **KEY** NS 1.2, MR 3.2

Find the value of n.

11. $n = 20\%$ of $100 _____

12. $n = 10\%$ of $80 _____

13. Addison finds a shirt on sale for 30% off the regular price of $50. How much will Addison save?

_____

Read a Map

Solve.

1. The Monkey House is located at (−1, 5). In what Quadrant is the Monkey House located? **Hint:** Remember the quadrants go counter clockwise.

   _____

2. The location of the zoo's concession stand can be found at (4, 1). Write the letter C at this location on the map.

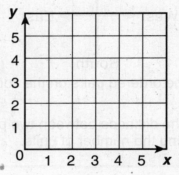

3. The zoo information booth is at the origin. Move 4 units to the west and 3 units to the north to the petting zoo. Write the ordered pair of the petting zoo.

   _____

4. The zoo gift shop is located at (4, 4) and the ice cream stand at (2, −1). Give directions from the gift shop to the ice cream stand.

   _____

   _____

5. The zoo is located at (−5, 4) and the art museum at (−5, −3). Each unit is equal to 3 miles. What is the distance in miles between the zoo and art museum?

   _____

6. Four tortoises were sleeping in different locations in the exhibit. Terri was asleep at (5, −1), Tasha at (2, −5), Trevor at (2, −1), and Thomas at (−4, 8). Which tortoise was sleeping furthest away from the origin?

   _____

Integers and Functions

CA Standards
AF 1.0, KEY AF 1.5

$y = 3x - 4$

Step 1 Copy the function table to show values of x and y from the function $y = 3x - 4$.

Step 2 Use the equation to find the missing y-values.

If $x = 1$, then $y = 3(1) - 4 = {}^{-}1$
If $x = 2$, then $y = 3(2) - 4 = 2$
If $x = 3$, then $y = 3(3) - 4 = 5$
If $x = 4$, then $y = 3(4) - 4 = 8$

$y = 3x - 4$

x	y
1	⁻1
2	2
3	5
4	8

Copy and complete each function table.

1. $y = x + 4$

x	y
⁻3	
⁻2	
⁻1	
0	

2. $y = x - 3$

x	y
⁻2	
0	
2	
5	

3. $y = 6 - x$

x	y
⁻2	
0	
2	
5	

4. $y = 4x$

x	y
0	
1	
2	
3	

5. $y = x - 6$

x	y
⁻3	
0	
3	
6	

6. $y = 7x$

x	y
0	
1	
2	
3	

Spiral Review (Chapter 15, Lesson 3 and Lesson 5) **KEY NS 2.2**

7. $45 \overline{)5535}$ _____

8. $31 \overline{)86366}$ _____

9. A potato chip factory produces 92,673 bags of chips each day. If the factory produces chips for 9 hours a day, how many bags of chips do they produce in each hour?

_____

Integers and Functions

Solve.

1. Becky is making cupcakes for her school's Bake Sale. She fills each box with 6 cupcakes. How many cupcakes are in 4 boxes?

Box	Number of Cupcakes
x	y
1	6
2	12
3	18
4	_____

_____

2. Punch is also being sold at the Bake Sale. Each hour 12 cups of punch is sold. How many cups of punch will be sold after 3 hours?

Hours	Number of cups of punch
x	y
1	12
2	24
3	_____
4	_____

_____

3. The function $y = 2x - 1$ describes the path a storm is taking. At noon, $x = 0$. Find the value of y at noon.

_____

4. The function $g = s + 30$ expresses Gloria's age (g) in terms of Stephanie's age (s). How old will Gloria be when Stephanie is 33?

_____

5. Coleman received 32 points from her first two tests in math. She scored 8 points more on her first test than her second test. What were her two test scores? Show the function that answers the question.

_____

_____

_____

6. Kathy is twice as old as Brian. Brian is 3 years younger than Mason. If Mason is 7 years old, how old are Kathy and Brian? Write equations to show your work. Write their ages in order from least to greatest.

_____

_____

_____

_____

Graph Functions and Integers

CA Standard
KEY AF 1.5

How to Graph an Equation

Step 1 Complete the function table.   **Step 2** Graph each ordered pair.   **Step 3** Extend the line.

Copy and complete the function table. Then graph the function in a coordinate plane.

1. $y = 4x - 2$

x	y
0	
1	
2	
3	

2. $y = 3x + 2$

x	y
0	
1	
2	
3	

Which of these ordered pairs are on the line described by $y = 2x + 5$?

3. $(1, 8)$ _____   **4.** $(^-3, ^-11)$ _____   **5.** $(1, 7)$ _____   **6.** $(^-4, ^-3)$ _____

7. Maria used the equation and table to graph the cost of renting a bicycle. If x represents the number of hours the bicycle is rented, and y represents the cost, what does her graph look like?

x	y
1	9
2	12
3	15

_____

Spiral Review   (Chapter 23, Lesson 4) **KEY** NS 1.2, MR 3.2

8. Find 18% of 64. _____   **9.** Find 80% of 37. _____

10. Maureen got 40% of her math test incorrect. If her test was 50 questions, how many questions did Maureen get incorrect?

_____

Graph Functions and Integers

Solve.

1. Use the equation and function table to graph the equation on the coordinate plane. $y = x + 6$

$y = x + 6$	
x	y
−2	_____
−1	_____
0	_____
1	_____

2. The equation represents the points earned or lost in a game. Use the equation to complete the function table.

$y = 2x - 5$	
x	y
−1	_____
0	_____
2	_____
4	_____

3. The equation $y = x - 4$ represents the number of coins Sarah has in her coin collection, if Stephen has x coins. If Stephen has 35 coins, how many coins does Sarah have?

_____

4. The equation $y = 2x + 1$ represents the number of blocks Michelle walks in x minutes. Michelle used the equation to make the table. Graph the equation on the coordinate plane.

x	y
1	3
2	5
3	7
4	9

5. The equation $y = 5x + 6$ can be used to find the cost of playing laser tag. Graph the function on the coordinate plane.

6. The equation $y = x - 3$ can be used to find the number of minutes it takes Drake to read a book. Graph the function on the coordinate plane.

Hands On: Linear Equations

CA Standards
KEY SDAP 1.5, **KEY** AF 1.5

How to Graph an Equation	
Step 1 Make a function table with *x* and *y* columns.	**Step 2** Graph each ordered pair.

Complete the steps to graph the equation $y = 3x + 2$ and check your work.

1. Make a function table. Use these values for *x*.

x	y
0	
1	
2	
3	

2. Write the ordered pairs.

_____

_____

3. Graph the equation.

4. Find two other points on the line and check to see if the coordinates make the equation true.

_____

_____

Spiral Review (Chapter 15, Lesson 5) **KEY NS 2.2**

5. $68 \overline{)23,596}$ _____

6. $35 \overline{)2,590}$ _____

7. Julian says that $73 \overline{)4,307}$ is 59. Greg says that the quotient is 95. Who is correct? Explain.

_____

_____

Hands On: Linear Equations

CA Standards
KEY SDAP 1.5, **KEY** AF 1.5

Solve Problems 1–6.

1. Use the equation and function table to graph the equation on the coordinate plane.

$y = 2x$	
x	**y**
−2	−4
−1	
0	
1	2

2. The equation represents the points earned or lost in a trivia game. Use the equation to complete the function table.

$y = x - 3$	
x	**y**
−1	
0	−3
2	
4	

3. The equation $y = 2x - 4$ represents the number of rocks Justin has in his rock collection, if Skip has x rocks. If Skip has 23 rocks, how many rocks does Justin have?

_____

_____

4. The equation $y = 5x + 8$ represents the number of miles Lennie jogs in x hours. Lennie used the equation to make this function table. Graph the equation on the coordinate plane.

x	**y**
1	13
2	18
3	23
4	28

5. The equation $y = 3x + 6$ can be used to find the cost of ice skating. Graph the equation on the coordinate plane.

6. Jake had this equation for homework: $y = -2x - 3$. Graph the equation on the coordinate plane.

Graphs of Formulas

George is helping his uncle move by packing toys into boxes. The length of each box is 7 inches and the height is 8 inches. To find how much each box will hold, George needs to find the volume using the formula $V = l \times w \times h$.

Make a graph to represent the formula
$V = 7 \times w \times 8$.

Step 1 Make a function table. Then write the ordered pairs.

Step 2 Plot the points on a coordinate grid.

V = 7 x w x 8	
w	V
5	280
6	336
7	392

(5, 280)

(6, 336)

(7, 392)

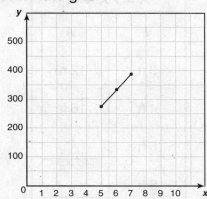

Solution: The formula can be represented by the graph shown above.

Use the graph above. Find V (volume) for each value of w (width). Use the formula to check your answer.

1. w = 8 in.

2. w = 10 in.

3. w = 30 in.

_____   _____   _____

Use the graph above. Find w (width) for each value of V (volume). Use the formula to check your answer.

4. V = 504 in.³

5. V = 672 in.³

6. V = 112 in.³

_____   _____   _____

Spiral Review   (Chapter 15, Lesson 5)   **KEY NS 2.2**

Divide.

7. 49) 15,533 _____

8. 86) 4,902 _____

9. In one month, 8,670 visitors attended an art gallery. Tours were given to groups of 15 visitors. How many tours were given?

_____

Graphs of Formulas

Solve Problems 1–6.

1. Corrie is ordering a rug for her living room. The rugs come in various sizes. Complete the function table to find the area of the rugs.

$A = l \times 4$ ft	
l	**A**
3 ft	12 ft²
4 ft	16 ft²
5 ft	_____
8 ft	_____

2. Mariko is looking to purchase a new fish tank. Complete the function table to find the volume of the tanks Mariko is looking at.

$V = l \times 2$ ft $\times 3$ ft	
l	**V**
2 ft	12 ft³
3 ft	18 ft³
4 ft	_____
5 ft	_____

3. Sandra used the formula $A = s^2$ to find the area of squares. Complete the function table to find the area of various squares.

$A = s^2$	
S	**A**
3	_____
5	_____
7	_____
9	_____

4. Use the function table in problem 3 to create a graph of the formula $A = s^2$.

_____

5. The formula for the circumference of a circle is $C = d \times \pi$. Use the formula to make a function table and create a graph.

_____

6. The area for a triangle is $\frac{1}{2}b \times h$. Use the formula to make a function table and create a graph.

_____

Write Equations for Lines

CA Standards
KEY AF 1.5, KEY SDAP 1.4

Write an equation when the graph has already been made.

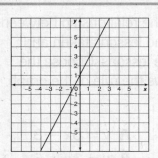

Monica drew this graph.

Which is the equation of Monica's line?

A $y = 3x + 1$ **C** $y = 2x + 1$

B $y = 3x + 2$ **D** $y = 2x + 13$

Step 1 Find three points that lie on the line. $(-1, -1)$, $(0, 1)$ and $(1, 3)$ are three points on the line.

Step 2 Test the ordered pairs in each equation. Remember that the equation must work for ALL of the ordered pairs.

Test Equation A $y = 3x + 1$	Test Equation B $y = 2x + 1$
$(-1, -1)$ $-1 \neq 3(-1) + 1$	$(-1, -1)$ $-1 = 2(-1) + 1$
	$(0, 1)$ $\quad 1 = 2(0) + 1$
	$(1, 3)$ $\quad 3 = 2(1) + 1$

Since the equation in choice B works, you do not need to test the other equations.

Solution: The equation of Monica's line is $y = 2x + 1$, choice C.

Write an equation for the graph.

1.

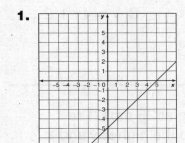

_____

2.

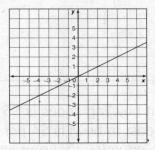

_____

Spiral Review (Chapter 23, Lesson 4) **KEY NS 1.2, MR 3.2**

Find each value.

3. 25 % of 160 _____

4. 65 % of 80 _____

5. Donna got 84% of the 50 questions on the test correct. How many questions did she answer correctly? _____

Write Equations for Lines

CA Standards
KEY AF 1.5, **KEY** SDAP 1.4

Solve Problems 1–6.

1. The graph shows the relationship between the amount Jeff saved and the number of weeks he saved. Write the equation for the graph.

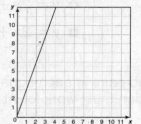

_____

2. The graph shows the relationship between the number of piano lessons taken and the total cost of the lessons. Choose the equation that shows the rule of the graph.

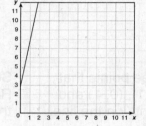

A $y = 5x - 3$

B $y = 3x + 5$

C $y = 5x + 3$

_____

3. The graph shows the relationship between the cost of play tickets and the number of people buying tickets. Write the equation for the graph.

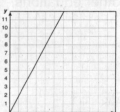

_____

4. The graph shows the relationship between the number of people in a paddle boat and the cost of renting a paddle boat. Choose the equation that shows the rule of the graph.

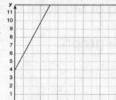

A $y = 2x - 4$

B $y = 2x + 4$

C $y = 4x + 2$

_____

5. The cost to rent bowling shoes is $5 per night. The cost to bowl is $4 per game. Write an equation that represents the cost of renting bowling shoes and playing x games in one night.

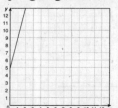

_____

6. A car is traveling at 25 mph. The driver turns onto the highway and begins to increase speed. The car's speed increases at a rate of 5 mph each second. Write an equation that represents the car's speed after x seconds.

_____

Equations of Horizontal and Vertical Lines

CA Standards
KEY AF 1.5, **KEY** AF 1.4

Graph the line $x = ^-7$.

Step 1 Make a function table. Choose 2 values for y. You already know the x-value is $^-7$.

$x = ^-7$	
x	y
$^-7$	2
$^-7$	1

Step 2 Plot the points in the coordinate plane and draw a line that passes through the points.

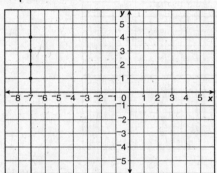

Step 3 Find 2 other points on the line and check to see if their x-coordinates are also $^-7$. Other points on the line include $(^-7, 3)$, $(^-7, 4)$.

Graph the line with the given equation.

1. $y = ^-1$

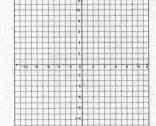

2. $x = 6$

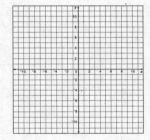

3. $y = 3$

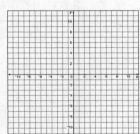

4. $y = ^-9$

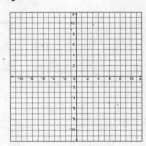

 **Spiral Review** (Chapter 27, Lesson 1) **KEY** AF 1.4, **KEY** SDAP 1.5

Use the coordinate grid. Write an ordered pair for each point.

5. Point R _____

6. Point S _____

7. Point P _____

8. Point Q _____

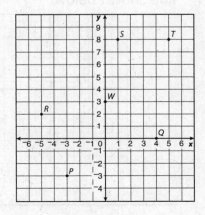

Equations of Horizontal and Vertical Lines

CA Standards
KEY AF 1.5, **KEY** AF 1.4

Solve.

1. Raquel plotted 3 points on a coordinate plane: (4, 8), (1, 8), (0, 8). What is the equation for the line?

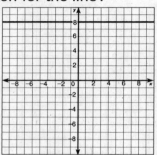

2. Gina says the equation for the line on this graph is $y = {}^-4$. Is she correct? Explain.

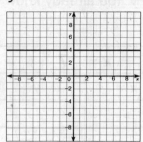

_____

3. Serena graphed a line that was parallel to the y-axis and contained the point (5, 2). What is the equation of Serena's line?

_____

4. Juan needs to graph a line with the equation $x = {}^-3$. Draw what Juan's line should look like.

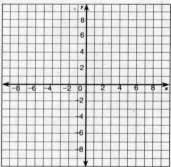

5. Write the equation represented by the line shown below.

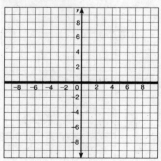

6. Look at both lines shown below. Which line represents the line $y = {}^-2$.

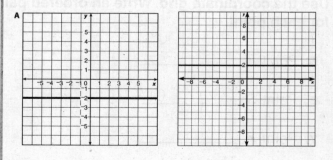

_____

Problem Solving: Use a Graph

CA Standards
MR 2.3, KEY SDAP 1.4

Mercury is the closest planet to the sun and is about the same size as the moon. It is covered with mountains, craters, ridges, and valleys. Mercury takes about 88 days to make one complete orbit around the sun. How many days does it take Mercury to make multiple orbits around the sun?

Number of Orbits (x)	Number of Days (y)
1	88
2	176
3	264
4	352

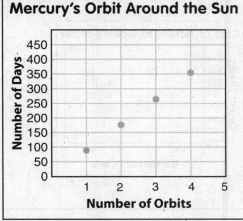

Mercury's Orbit Around the Sun

Step 1 Use the table to write ordered pairs: (1, 88), (2, 176), (3, 264), (4, 352).

Step 2 Graph the given coordinates.

Solve. Use the graph. Explain why your answer makes sense.

1. The graph and the table show the relationship between the number of orbits and the number of days it takes for Mercury to orbit around the sun. What information is displayed on the x-axis?

_____

2. Use the graph and the table to find the number of days it would take for Mercury to orbit around the sun five times.

_____

Spiral Review (Chapter 27, Lesson 1) **KEY SDAP 1.5**

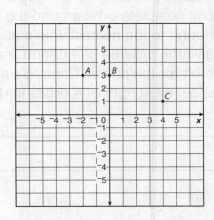

Write the ordered pair for each point.

3. A _____

4. B _____

5. Andre drew point C on the grid. What is the ordered pair for point C?

_____

Use with text pp. 616–617

Problem Solving: Use a Graph

CA Standards
MR 2.3, **KEY** SDAP 1.4

Solve.

1. Use the graph below to find the amount Julie would spend for 3 tickets to the Galaxy Show.

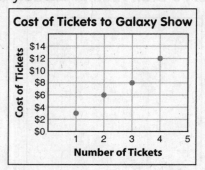

Cost of Tickets to Galaxy Show

Cost of Tickets / Number of Tickets

_____

2. Henry and his three friends each bought tickets to the Galaxy Show. How much money did they spend all together?

_____

_____

3. The Science Center posted this table to list the cost of admission tickets. How much would it cost for 6 people to enter the Science Center?

Number of Tickets	1	2	3	4
Cost of Ticket(s)	$7	$14	$21	$28

_____

4. Andrew used the table in 3 to plot ordered pairs on a graph: (1, 7), (2, 14), (3, 21), (4, 28), (5, 34). Describe his mistake.

_____

_____

_____

5. It takes Neptune 164.79 years to make one complete orbit around the sun. Round to the nearest whole number and give the ordered pair of one complete orbit for the planet. Complete a graph to show the length of 4 orbits for the planet.

_____

_____

6. Raphael found this chart in a science book. Use the information to create a graph to display the data.

Distances between Planets and the Sun

Mercury: 36 million miles

Venus: 67 million miles

Earth: 93 million miles

Mars: 142 million miles